The Farm Bureau
and the New Deal

*This book is the 1961
award winner of the*

AGRICULTURAL
HISTORY SOCIETY

(No award was made in 1960)

The Farm Bureau

A Study of the Making of
National Farm Policy
1933-40

By
Christiana McFadyen
Campbell

University of Illinois Press
Urbana 1962

and the New Deal

To my father

Preface 🌿 ≪≪

In this study I have attempted to throw some light upon the making of public policy for agriculture during the years 1933-40 by examining the history of the American Farm Bureau Federation during that period. The Farm Bureau was by all odds the most influential of the farm organizations in those crucial years, when the basic principles of the New Deal for agriculture were enacted into law or embedded in administrative practices.

This manuscript is substantially the same as the dissertation which I presented for the Ph.D. degree at the University of Chicago in 1960. I carried out much of the basic research in 1948-49. Subsequently I went to live in Australia, and there wrote the greater portion of the manuscript. In 1959 I took advantage of an opportunity to return to the United States for twelve months. This enabled me to work in additional manuscript collections, to interview several key people with whom I had not previously talked, and to rewrite the entire manuscript.

The chief sources used in this study were the papers in the files of the American Farm Bureau Federation at its headquarters in Chicago, especially those having to do with the O'Neal administration. To these I was granted free access in 1948-49, and I spent the greater part of that academic year carrying on research in them. I undertook to examine these papers in the spirit of objective scholarship, and this was understood by the officers and staff of the American Farm Bureau Federation. I wish to express my deepest appreciation for the many courtesies they showed me.

In an attempt to gain a balanced point of view, I used some of the papers of the Department of Agriculture now in the National Archives. Among the most useful of these were the Correspondence of the Secretary of Agriculture and the Records of the Agricultural Adjustment Administration.

I also visited the home of Edward A. O'Neal in Florence, Alabama, to talk with him and to use the small collection of his personal papers which were then (in 1949) in his possession there. Other Farm Bureau leaders whom I interviewed were James R. Howard of Iowa, Earl C. Smith of Illinois, Howard E. Babcock of New York, Walter Randolph of Alabama, Allan B. Kline of Iowa, and Charles Shuman of Illinois. The following persons who were in the Department of Agriculture during the period 1933-40 also talked with me about the issues and events of that time: Henry A. Wallace, Rexford G. Tugwell, Paul H. Appleby, M. L. Wilson, and James G. Maddox. To all the people who granted me interviews, I express my appreciation of their patience and generosity.

That my work does not afford a complete explanation of farm policy-making during the New Deal period I should be the first to recognize. Studies of other farm organizations need to be made, and the relationships between farm and non-farm interest groups need to be much further explored. But if farm policy-making during the New Deal period cannot be explained solely in terms of the Farm Bureau's role, neither can it be explained without close examination of that role. This study is offered in the hope that others will build upon it.

I owe a special debt to each of the three members of my dissertation committee. Professor Avery O. Craven, who has been my adviser for many years, directed my attention toward the larger setting of farm policy in American history. Professor William T. Hutchinson made careful and specific suggestions about the style, form, and content of the manuscript. From its inception, this study has received every encouragement and invaluable assistance from Professor Theodore W. Schultz. He has given generously of his time in talking with me about the Farm Bureau, and in directing my attention to significant issues and sources. I am indebted to him for many stimulating ideas.

Dr. Gladys Baker of the United States Department of Agriculture and my friend Mrs. Katharine Burks gave me important help in introducing me to the sources available in Washington, D.C.

The unfailing encouragement of my husband Keith Campbell has enabled me to complete this manuscript.

While all the above people and many others have assisted in this study, the author is solely responsible for the interpretations and conclusions presented herein.

CHRISTIANA McFADYEN CAMPBELL

Sydney, Australia
October, 1961

Contents

Introduction 🌿 ⋘

It has sometimes been more difficult to secure agreement among farmers on national farm policy than it has been to persuade Congress and the Administration to adopt such policy. The most significant role played by the American Farm Bureau Federation during the New Deal period was as one of the more important agencies through which agreement within agriculture was achieved. Most especially, the national Farm Bureau leaders in the 1930's took pride in establishing and preserving the sectional alliance between the agricultural Midwest and the agricultural South, on which the power of the American Farm Bureau Federation chiefly depended. This task of bringing about unity within agriculture, however, was only a necessary means to an end—that of maintaining sufficient strength in the national arena to achieve compromises between agriculture and other interest groups, such as labor and business, in the making of national economic policy.[1]

During the period of this study, 1933 through 1940, the American Farm Bureau Federation achieved considerable success in bridging the sectional, commodity, and partisan political conflicts within agriculture, thus establishing the basis for power which made it one of the most important influences in Washington in the days of the New Deal.

But whether the American Farm Bureau Federation was a central force in the making of the New Deal for agriculture, or conversely, whether the power of the American Farm Bureau Federation was largely an outgrowth of the New Deal for agriculture, has been the subject of bitter controversy.

---

[1] As early as 1787, *The Federalist*, especially essays Nos. 10 and 51 by James Madison, gave a penetrating analysis of the necessity for the reconciliation of conflicting economic interests through government. A twentieth-century interpretation which offers considerable insight is found in the theory of countervailing power propounded in J. K. Galbraith, *American Capitalism* (Boston: Houghton Mifflin Co., 1952). "Not until farmers and workers achieved some organization on their own behalf were they able to get the state to reinforce their efforts," says Galbraith (p. 155).

CHAPTER I

Origins and Functions

One of the phenomena of twentieth-century American history is the genesis of the Farm Bureau as a crusading educational agency, and its evolution in less than a quarter of a century into an extraordinarily influential force in the political arena. In the course of this evolution the Farm Bureau developed the ambivalent nature—at once crusading and ruthless—which is displayed most strikingly in the New Deal period. The fact that Farm Bureau had its sources in two quite disparate streams of American history probably accounts for this persistent ambivalence. One of these streams was the mounting enthusiasm for scientific agriculture and its concomitant, agricultural education, which has held a place in American intellectual and social history since the time of Thomas Jefferson.[1] The other was the trend, so marked in the twentieth century, toward the organization of economic groups on a national scale.

The first local farm bureau was established in 1911, and by 1915 county farm bureaus were so numerous that state federations began to be formed. In 1919-20 the state federations joined in organizing the American Farm Bureau Federation.[2]

Unlike previous farmers' movements, the Farm Bureau has flourished best in times of prosperity. The membership figures clearly show this. The lowest ebb in Farm Bureau membership was reached in the depression of 1929-33. Thus, at the beginning of the New Deal period Farm Bureau membership was at its nadir.

[1] For a summary of early means of agricultural education, see Gladys Baker, *The County Agent* (Chicago: University of Chicago Press, 1939), pp. 1-45; and Everett E. Edwards, "American Agriculture—the First 300 Years," in *Farmers in a Changing World*, Yearbook of the U.S. Department of Agriculture for 1940 (Washington: Government Printing Office, 1940), pp. 246-56.

[2] Orville M. Kile, *The Farm Bureau Through Three Decades* (Baltimore: The Waverly Press, 1948), pp. 47-57.

TABLE 1

Membership of the American Farm Bureau Federation, 1920-48 [a]

Year	Number of Members	Year	Number of Members	Year	Number of Members
1920	317,108	1930	321,196	1940	444,485
1921	466,422	1931	276,053	1941	518,031
1922	363,481	1932	205,348	1942	591,230
1923	392,581	1933	163,246	1943	687,499
1924	301,747	1934	222,557	1944	828,486
1925	314,474	1935	280,916	1945	986,136
1926	278,759	1936	356,563	1946	1,128,259
1927	272,047	1937	409,766	1947	1,275,180
1928	301,700	1938	396,799	1948	1,325,826
1929	301,932	1939	398,197		

[a] Source: Compiled by Dorothy Davis, Assistant Director of Information, A.F.B.F., from the annual reports of the treasurer. Farm Bureau memberships are family memberships, unlike the Grange, where husband and wife hold separate memberships.

The Farm Bureau originated in a golden age of American agriculture, that of the period 1909-14. The policy of "parity," which came to epitomize the A.F.B.F.'s goal during the New Deal period,[3] was essentially an effort to re-establish the relative position that agriculture had held during that golden age.

However, the first farm bureau did not originate under prosperous conditions. It was organized in Binghamton, Broome County,[4] in upstate New York, a region which was even then threatened by farm abandonment, a trend which had already engulfed much of New England agriculture. Agricultural reformers of that day believed that the way to save such farms was to demonstrate how to make "two blades of grass to grow upon a spot of ground where only one grew before," in accordance with the maxim of Jonathan Swift, which they particularly cherished.[5] The abandoned farms which today characterize the very area in which the first farm bureau was established attest both the need for agrarian reform there and the futility of the efforts to stem that particular tide.

---

[3] The aim of parity was to re-establish the purchasing power of farmers at what it had been in some base period. The gist of the concept was that prices received for farm commodities should bear an equitable relationship to prices paid for commodities which farmers bought. This ratio was assumed to be equitable if it were the same as it had been in a selected base period. During the early New Deal, the base period, except for tobacco, was 1909-14.

[4] Kile, *op. cit.*, pp. 36-40.

[5] The heart of the gospel of agricultural education comes, surprisingly, from *Gulliver's Travels*.

The first farm bureau was not a typical one for it was a bureau of the local chamber of commerce.[6] It did, however, employ a county agricultural agent, to whom the New York State College of Agriculture acted as general adviser.[7] Moreover, it gave the name "Farm Bureau" to the movement. Many farmers being suspicious of the motives of businessmen, the Broome County organization separated from the chamber of commerce in 1914,[8] and the Farm Bureau movement on the whole has had no special connection with the U.S. Chamber of Commerce. The first farmer organization which more nearly set the pattern for the later farm bureaus was that established in Pettis County, Missouri, in 1912. By 1913 this organization had a financial relationship with both the Missouri College of Agriculture and with the U.S. Department of Agriculture.[9]

The real beginning of the Farm Bureau movement, however, came not in 1911 but in 1914, with the establishment of the federal-state Agricultural Extension Service.[10] The Smith-Lever Act of 1914 is almost as much a charter for the Farm Bureau as it is for the Extension Service. This act of Congress made federal funds available on a grant-in-aid basis to states for agricultural education through the county agent system.

Many of the early county agents were enthusiastic about organizing local farmers into farm bureaus, and state Extension Service directors encouraged them, particularly in the northern and western states.[11] These early farm bureaus were considered useful media through which the county agent could spread his gospel of scientific agriculture. Moreover, many of the county agents were also imbued with the idea that farmers must organize if they were to survive in a world of organized business and organized labor. To help farmers organize and develop leadership among themselves was considered a worthy end in itself.[12]

Several state legislatures, in authorizing state aid to match federal funds, stipulated that county farm bureaus could or should be organized, and that the county agent should work through them. New York state was the most outstanding instance of this sort of arrange-

---

[6] Kile, *op. cit.*, pp. 36-40.

[7] Baker, *op. cit.*, pp. 15-16.

[8] Kile, *op. cit.*, pp. 39-40.

[9] Baker, *op. cit.*, p. 16.

[10] There were some county agricultural agents in existence previously, but following the passage of the Smith-Lever Act their work was expanded and systematized. *Ibid.*, p. 8.

[11] *Ibid.*, p. 16.

[12] M. L. Wilson, personal interview, August 29, 1959.

ment. In other states the law required an organization of farmers of above a minimum number, before appropriations could be made to the Extension Service, but did not specify that it should be a farm bureau. However, in actual practice county farm bureaus acted in that capacity in such important states as Iowa and Missouri. In still another group of states the legislature required an organization of farmers as sponsors for Extension work, but specified neither the particular organization nor the number of members. However, farm bureaus were able to take advantage of such laws in a number of states to sign agreements with the state Extension Service which gave them a monoply of the sponsorship role. The Illinois Agricultural Association, the strongest of the state farm bureaus in terms of membership, was in this position.[13]

Since contributions from private sources were specifically recognized in the Smith-Lever Act of 1914 as legitimate sources of state-matching funds,[14] in some areas county appropriations and farm bureau membership dues came to make up a substantial portion of the funds used for the county agent's salary and his work.[15] Thus the informal impulse for the promotion of farm bureaus by the Extension Service was reinforced in some cases by legal ties.

The entrance of the United States into World War I gave an enormous impetus to the county agent system and the Farm Bureau movement. The need for efficient agricultural production to feed both the United States and its allies prompted an increase in federal funds to extend the county agent system. The number of county agents was multiplied, and many county agents in turn considered it virtually a patriotic duty to organize farm bureaus. This was particularly true in the Midwest and Northeast.

In her definitive study of the county agent, Gladys Baker concludes that the organization of county farm bureaus during World War I "laid the framework for that anomalous, powerful, semipublic organization, the American Farm Bureau Federation."[16]

About this time, some of the leaders of the other farm organizations, the Grange, the Farmers' Union, the Nonpartisan League, began to look with some trepidation upon this development. Their fear that a rival general farm organization was being fostered by government agencies was allayed by assurances from the county agents

[13] William J. Block, *The Separation of the Farm Bureau and the Extension Service* (Urbana: University of Illinois Press, 1960), pp. 17-18.
[14] Baker, *op. cit.*, pp. 15-16.
[15] Kile, *op. cit.*, p. 16.
[16] Baker, *op. cit.*, p. 44.

that the farm bureaus were for educational purposes only.[17] In the circumstances, it was difficult to protest further.

The county agents were perfectly honest in their assurances that the function of the farm bureaus was solely an educational one. Many of the county agents themselves began to be alarmed when county farm bureaus began to organize state federations. When the state federations formed the A.F.B.F., some Extension Service leaders considered this action nothing less than tragic.[18] However, Extension leaders in the northern and western states encouraged the organization of state farm bureau federations,[19] and the National County Agents Association, at a meeting in December, 1918, sponsored the movement to federate county farm bureaus into state and national federations.[20]

In the meantime, a new type of state farm bureau had already come into being, pioneered in 1916 by the organization of the Illinois Agricultural Association. Not only education, but business activities and legislation were recognized from the very beginning as legitimate and primary functions of this state farm bureau. Thus the pattern of the Farm Bureau as an appendage of the Extension Service, carrying on purely educational functions, was broken.[21] The Illinois setup came to be viewed with admiration and respect in Farm Bureau circles. During his presidency of the A.F.B.F., Edward A. O'Neal of Alabama considered it the ideal.

With the organization of the A.F.B.F. in 1919-20, and with emphasis shifting in some states to new functions, the relationship between the Farm Bureau and the Extension Service began to change.

From being an Extension-dominated organization, the Farm Bureau henceforward achieved a greater independence and in some cases actually dominated the county agents. The true relationship did not depend upon the presence or absence of legal ties. In Alabama, where no legal tie existed, the state Extension Service continued to control the state Farm Bureau. In Illinois, where the closest of legal ties was maintained, the farm bureau had the upper hand, at least on the county level. In most cases the relationship was not so clear-cut. Usually it became one of informal reciprocity between two more or less separate organizations, through a tacit

---

[17] M. L. Wilson, personal interview, August 29, 1959.
[18] *Ibid.*
[19] Baker, *op. cit.*, p. 17.
[20] *Ibid.*, p. 18.
[21] *Ibid.*

gentlemen's agreement by which the Farm Bureau gave political support to the Extension Service, and the Extension Service in turn gave whatever aid it could to the Farm Bureau. However, in some states, notably where other farm organizations were strong, the Extension directors refused to show any partiality to the Farm Bureau.

In Pennsylvania and in some Southern states, the Extension directors were hostile to the idea of sponsoring the Farm Bureau.[22]

In the early phase of the movement, the strength of the Farm Bureau lay in the Midwest and the Northeast, where it had been originally fostered by the Extension Service. Except in Alabama and Tennessee, the organization of farm bureaus was not encouraged by Southern state Extension directors in the early period, and the Farm Bureau movement was particularly weak in the South before 1933.[23]

The organization of the A.F.B.F. came comparatively late in the era of the organization of economic groups on a national scale. The "nationalizing of business" had already taken place in the late nineteenth century. The trend to corporate organization of business had not, however, carried over to any appreciable extent into agriculture. While the concentration of business into fewer and fewer firms was going on, agricultural land continued predominantly to be owned as individual proprietorships and operated in relatively small units. To offset the concentrated power of business, there was no comparable concentration of power in either agriculture or labor. The power status of farmers was further weakened vis-à-vis both business and labor by the decline in the farm population, which was a relative decline before 1910, and an absolute decline, except for temporary spurts, thereafter. Before 1919, labor, though far behind business, was already well on its way to effective national organization through the American Federation of Labor. There were, it is true, several farm organizations claiming national membership in existence before 1919, but these had either expired (e.g., the Farmers

----

[22] Attempts were made by various Secretaries of the U.S. Department of Agriculture to limit the participation of Extension Service personnel in the Farm Bureau specifically to educational activities. Finally, in 1954, Secretary Benson issued a directive forbidding employees of the Department of Agriculture from engaging in a list of activities which amounted, in essence, to promoting any general or specialized organization of farmers. Thus formal ties were apparently cut altogether, but whether the informal alliance between the Extension Service and the Farm Bureau still exists is another matter. See U.S. Department of Agriculture, Office of the Secretary, Memorandum No. 1368, November 24, 1954. For an extensive treatment of the separation of the Farm Bureau from the Extension Service, see Block, *op. cit.*

[23] Baker, *op. cit.*, p. 20.

Alliance), passed their prime (e.g., the Grange), or failed as yet to develop significance (e.g., the National Farmers' Union). When he went to Washington in 1920 to set up the legislative office of the A.F.B.F., the first president of this organization, James R. Howard, says that he found representatives of about 600 national organizations already there, about two-thirds of them with agricultural sections claiming to represent farmers.[24]

The prime function of the A.F.B.F., almost from its very beginning in 1919, has been to make, or to influence, national agricultural policy. Since makers of economic policy in the twentieth century typically have used the state as their chief medium, the Farm Bureau Federation naturally has emphasized policy-making through political action. This was a departure from the guiding idea of the original Farm Bureau movement in its local stages.

There was, however, a period around 1923 when the main emphasis of the A.F.B.F., under the influence of Aaron Sapiro, was on economic action through co-operative marketing, rather than on political action. Since then the commercial activities of the Farm Bureau have shifted from marketing co-operatives to the so-called "commercial services." Important among these have been Farm Bureau–affiliated co-operatives serving the needs of farmers as purchasers of farm supplies, such as petroleum products. Farm Bureau–affiliated insurance companies or co-operatives also have performed a major service in some states, in offering more economical or otherwise more advantageous terms to farmer members in such fields as life, automobile, fire, and crop insurance. The success, and the genuine saving to farmer members, of some of the Farm Bureau automobile insurance companies, for instance, has been spectacular. Most of the farm supply co-operatives and the insurance companies have been sponsored and controlled by state farm bureaus, but the A.F.B.F. has assisted and encouraged and sought to co-ordinate them.[25]

The commercial services of the state farm bureau were particularly successful in Illinois. Earl C. Smith, President of the Illinois Agricultural Association, was noted for his success in promoting the

---

[24] James R. Howard, "Memoirs" (unpublished manuscript in possession of Mr. Howard, Clemons, Iowa); also personal interview, June 22-23, 1949.

[25] This assistance was chiefly of an informal sort until 1945, when the A.F.B.F. set up a separate insurance department. In 1948 the A.F.B.F. assisted the state farm bureau fire and casualty companies in organizing a national re-insurance company known as the American Agricultural Insurance Company. Kile, *op. cit.*, pp. 346, 352.

farm bureau's business activities. Yet Earl Smith himself believed that the commercial services should be subordinate to legislative activities. He warned his fellow Midwestern leaders against over-emphasis on commercial services: "The basic philosophy of farm organization must be sold to farmers—Our members are not yet completely sold. . . . Some of you are overemphasizing commercial services—They are about 25% of the value of farm organization—Representation of farmers in economic matters is 75%—Income of dues should go to furnish leaders to study problems and get the right answers—Commercial services are incidental. There is no sub-stitute for membership dues."[26]

Other subsidiary but by no means unimportant functions have been of a recreational and welfare nature. While in general the Farm Bureau has not sought to serve purely social or recreational ends to nearly the same extent as has the Grange, certain local farm bureau units, particularly among the Associated Women's groups, have quite successfully performed this function. The Associated Women have also exercised some influence on the policies of the A.F.B.F. with respect to rural welfare. They were, for instance, credited by President O'Neal of the Farm Bureau with the responsi-bility for changing the federation's position on the Child Labor Amendment in 1935 from one of opposition to one of approval.[27] In the Farm Bureau proper, the promotion of rural welfare, not only through legislation but through such other means as state farm bu-reau sponsorship of group hospital-insurance schemes for farm people, has been a function of increasing importance.

The Farm Bureau has also enthusiastically encouraged the 4-H Club movement, which under Extension leadership serves some im-portant educational and recreational needs of rural young people. In many instances the 4-H Club movement has been given financial support by local farm bureaus.

The multiplicity and complexity of the functions of the Farm Bu-reau movement preclude any exclusive interpretation of the history of the organization, even during a limited period. Yet so far as the national federation is concerned, all the other functions, significant

---

[26] "Minutes of the Midwest Presidents' and Secretaries' Conference, Des Moines, Iowa, February 21, 1940," A.F.B.F. files, folder marked "Midwest Conferences, 1940."

[27] Letter from Edward A. O'Neal to E. S. Foster, General Secretary of the New York Farm Bureau, January 7, 1936, in A.F.B.F. files, President O'Neal Papers (hereafter referred to as A.F.B.F., O'Neal Papers). Unless otherwise indicated, all correspondence cited is from this collection.

though some of them were, have been usually minor ones compared to that of making and influencing American agricultural policy through political action.

Farm Bureau policy-makers have emphasized chiefly the role of farmers as producers for the market place. The conception of the A.F.B.F. chiefly as a producers' organization is confirmed by the overwhelming emphasis placed by the national federation on policies having to do with the prices of farm products. Typical of Farm Bureau statements of this point of view is that one approved by the executive committee of the A.F.B.F. and made by President O'Neal to the House Committee on Agriculture in 1937, which begins: "For many years the major objective of the American Farm Bureau Federation has been to secure fair stable prices for the producers of farm products."[28] Similarly, in favoring the reduction of appropriations for the Farm Security Administration, in 1944, O'Neal explained, incidentally: "The fact is that the best rural rehabilitation the Government could offer would be to permit farmers to realize fair prices in the market place."[29] Above all, the virtual cult of "parity," of which A.F.B.F. leaders were the leading oracles in the New Deal period, symbolizes the overwhelming importance of price policy.

However, the A.F.B.F.'s conception of its role as a producers' organization was not accepted without sharp challenge from within the Farm Bureau. The Ohio Farm Bureau, under the influence of its dynamic executive secretary, Murray Lincoln, who was also a member of the board of directors of the A.F.B.F., long sought to persuade O'Neal to recognize the voluntary consumer co-operative movement as a basic force. For instance, in 1936 he earnestly recommended to O'Neal the book by Marquis Childs, *Sweden, the Middle Way,* as an explication of successful consumer co-operation.[30] O'Neal obligingly created a committee to study the consumer co-operative movement and made Lincoln a member of it. When Lincoln discovered that Earl Smith had been appointed chairman, he wrote in affectionate exasperation to O'Neal, whom he still apparently hoped to convert, that he understood one way virtually to nullify any effective consideration by a committee was to name a

---

[28] A.F.B.F., "Minutes of the Executive Committee," *Minutes of the Board of Directors,* July 26, 1937.

[29] U.S. House of Representatives, Subcommittee of the Committee on Appropriations, *Hearings on Agriculture Department Appropriation Bill for 1945,* 78th Cong., 2d Sess., 1944, p. 1473.

[30] Lincoln to O'Neal, July 3, 1936.

chairman who was opposed to the matter.[31] O'Neal, in his reply, good-humoredly indicated that Lincoln's analysis was correct.[32] Thus, typically, the Ohio Farm Bureau had practically no success in winning over O'Neal personally or the A.F.B.F. officially to the consumer co-operative way. Certainly the Farm Bureau movement always had been and still continued to be a major force in promoting farm supply co-operatives, but the idea of joining in a movement to solve national economic problems by emphasizing the role of the consumer met with a cold reception on the part of the majority of the board of directors of the A.F.B.F. Lincoln himself acknowledged that it was "too much to hope that the A.F.B.F., because of its producer-mindedness," would take the lead in this movement.[33]

In performing its chosen function of making, or influencing, farm policy, the A.F.B.F. has at all times encountered competition, and sometimes very strong competition, from other agricultural organizations or institutions. These rivals, like the Farm Bureau, would like to be recognized as "the voice of the farmer." Among them have been not only the other two national general farm organizations— the National Grange and the National Farmers' Union—but powerful marketing co-operatives, which speak sometimes separately, sometimes through the National Council of Farmer Co-operatives (known as the Co-op Council). One of these co-operatives in particular, the Milk Producers' Federation, has been powerful enough to be considered a separate rival to the Farm Bureau and the other general farm organizations. The complexity of agricultural politics, once aptly described by O'Neal in a letter to George N. Peek as "wheels within wheels,"[34] embraces no more fascinating and significant aspect than that of the ever-shifting relationships among farm organizations. Frequently, when there was agreement on policy, the officers of these organizations worked harmoniously together to attain their common goals. For instance, such unity among the big farm organizations, with the exception of the National Farmers' Union, marked the early New Deal period. In fact, unity was most likely to exist during periods of depression or threatened depression. During his term as president of the Farm Bureau, O'Neal was most active in promoting conferences among farm organization leaders, and in attempting to achieve unity on the farm

---

[31] Lincoln to O'Neal, September 22, 1936.
[32] O'Neal to Lincoln, September 26, 1936.
[33] Lincoln to O'Neal, July 3, 1936.
[34] O'Neal to Peek, August 3, 1943.

organization front. It was always clearly understood, however, that these conferences were merely councils of diplomats, and that no farm organization leader could agree to co-operate on a policy of which his organization did not approve. Moreover, relationships among farm organizations, even when friendly, were always on a wary basis, for any policy had to be considered not only on its own merits but also from the point of view of whether its adoption would contribute to the power and influence of a rival farm organization. Farm Bureau leaders therefore exercised constant vigilance lest some farm policy should result in the creation of a new general farm organization, or the enlargement of the power of one of the existing general farm organizations to such an extent that the influence of the Farm Bureau would be threatened or destroyed. Other farm organization leaders no doubt exercised similar vigilance. The National Grange, for instance, while co-operating with and in fact following the lead of the Farm Bureau on many New Deal farm policies, nevertheless fought bitterly to separate the Extension Service from the Farm Bureau, believing that the tie between those two organizations had contributed unfairly to the power of the Farm Bureau.

Rival voices who would speak for the farmer in the making of national agricultural policy were to be found not only in other farm organizations but in the agricultural press (especially in the Association of Agricultural Editors), and in governmental and semi-governmental agencies, such as the Association of State Governors.

CHAPTER II

Structure

The structure of the A.F.B.F. was particularly well adapted to the political role which the organization sought to play. This was especially so because both the American government and the American Farm Bureau are based upon a federal system.

The formal structure of power within the A.F.B.F. was that of representative government. The states elected delegates to the A.F.B.F.'s annual meeting, and at this meeting resolutions governing the policies of the federation were discussed and adopted. An elective board of directors, composed of regional representatives and one representative of the Associated Women, met with the president and vice-president of the federation to decide on policy in the interim.[1] In addition there was an executive committee of the board which could meet on short notice. The president also directed a large staff of employees at the national headquarters of the federation in Chicago, as well as in the office of the Washington representative. Among the more important of the employees were the secretary, the director of information, and the Washington representative—the latter being lobbyist-in-chief for the federation, except when a president like O'Neal was his own chief lobbyist and the Washington representative was his assistant.

At one period in Farm Bureau history, some of the employees of the federation got out of hand, and came very close to running the association. Soon after O'Neal became president of the federation, he complained to the board of directors that the secretary (M. S. Winder) was calling himself an executive secretary, and was preventing the president from exercising his proper authority. O'Neal

---

[1] The board of directors' meeting was also attended regularly during the early period by the director of the U.S. Extension Service. Later on M. L. Wilson attended occasionally. Kile, *op. cit.*, p. 57.

made it plain that Winder must go, for the new president was not a man to be content with the shadow of authority.[2] The board gave full support to O'Neal in his efforts to re-establish the authority of the elective officers over that of the employees. Secretary Winder's resignation was accepted, and the employment of Director of Information Kibler was terminated. It is clear that their departure was not entirely a voluntary one, though it was accomplished quietly.[3] After that time, O'Neal had the loyal support of the federation's employees, many of whom were devoted to "the cause" of the Farm Bureau, and some of whom had been with the federation from the beginning.

The A.F.B.F. has customarily sought help from expert economists, both by employing reputable economists on its own staff and by formal and informal contacts with university staff members. These practices were in accord with the advice of Henry C. Wallace, who attended the organization meeting of the federation, and who admonished the Farm Bureau not to depend upon committees of farmers but to employ experts.[4] Whether the officers of the Farm Bureau Federation have taken the expert advice of intellectuals is another matter, but they have customarily sought it and respected it. Among the distinguished economists who have been employed on the regular staff of the federation have been J. K. Galbraith and T. K. Cowden. (However, Galbraith came to the Farm Bureau late in the New Deal period and Cowden came even later.)

Within the annual meeting, and also within the board of directors' meetings, the Farm Bureau's decisions have been traditionally reached by the process of majority rule. The Farm Bureau's officers have been proudly conscious of this fact, and even the most determined member of the board, when beaten on a major resolution affecting policy, has been loyal to the democratic process, accepting defeat ruefully though philosophically with some such remark as: "I stubbed my toe that time. Well, that's democracy." Not so loyal was the remark by a Southern member on an occasion when the Midwestern point of view prevailed on the board: "They may have us beaten here, but we have got them beaten in Congress."[5]

---

[2] A.F.B.F., *Minutes of the Board of Directors,* December 7-8, 1933.

[3] Their departure was also undoubtedly associated with the exposure by a Senate committee of their activities in connection with ship subsidies. A.F.B.F., "Minutes of the Executive Committee," *ibid.,* October 29, 1933.

[4] Wallace is quoted in Kile, *op. cit.,* p. 56. Henry C. Wallace, father of Henry A. Wallace, was Secretary of Agriculture under President Harding.

[5] These were remarks made after a board of directors' meeting in 1949,

The Farm Bureau Federation has been remarkably open about its debates and decisions. Farm Bureau leaders and staff have been proud of the fact that an association composed of so many farmers could have no secrets. Nevertheless, certain activities of several of the employed staff of the federation were not known even to Farm Bureau members until revealed to the public in the Congressional investigations of lobbying in connection with Muscle Shoals.[6] The financial connections thus revealed between several Farm Bureau employees as well as an ex-employee and certain big corporations (especially the American Cyanamid Company) amounted to a near scandal, and caused lasting damage to the good name of the Farm Bureau. The whole thing was looked upon as a bad mistake by the bona fide farmer members and leaders of the organization, and one from which the Farm Bureau must guard itself in the future—both by exercising more stringent control over the employed staff and also by avoiding "jackpot" financing agreements with other organizations.

The actual loci of power within the Farm Bureau are, naturally enough, not revealed by the formal structure. Throughout the history of the federation, overwhelming power has undoubtedly been centered in the board of directors. This was composed chiefly of the presidents, or in some cases secretaries, of the most powerful state federations, regionally represented.

Under these circumstances, leadership and the personality of leaders often assumed a major role in policy-making. To many people, President Edward A. O'Neal and Vice-President Earl C. Smith *were* the Farm Bureau during the period of Roosevelt's New Deal.

It was common knowledge, moreover, that the resolutions committee for the annual meeting, appointed by President O'Neal but dominated by its chairman, Earl Smith, was a major force in determining the policies of the association. This was simply one of the facts taken for granted by all who knew the inner workings of the Farm Bureau.

In actuality, then, the Farm Bureau's cherished belief that its policy was made at the grass roots and adopted by a democratic process turns out to be partly illusion. Decisions were largely made

---

which the author was allowed to attend as an observer. The first remark is the more typical.

[6] See, for instance, U.S. Senate, Committee on the Judiciary, *Hearings on Lobby Investigation*, 71st Cong., 2d Sess., sec. 2, part 7 (February 18, 19, 20, 21, 25, 26, 27, 28, and March 4, 5, 6, 7, 1930), pp. 2819-37, 3048.

by the board of directors, under the leadership of the forceful vice-president and the persuasive president.

To characterize the A.F.B.F., however, as an oligarchy, as a recent writer has done,[7] is unwarranted, for the power of the Farm Bureau has lain in the states. It has been a decentralized organization, despite the dominating leadership manifest by the board of directors of the federation. No director could commit his state or region to a policy unless he could count on support for it back home. During the period of the New Deal, directors like Romeo Short of Arkansas and Murray Lincoln of Ohio were not docile dependents of O'Neal and Earl Smith, but were powers in their own right. The task of O'Neal and Smith was to persuade the directors to accept compromises involving the interests of their regions. In turn, the directors had both to represent the interests of their regions in the board meetings and to "educate" their people back home in the policies of "the American" (as the federation was called). In 1933 the Washington representative, Chester Gray, told the board: "intricate propositions like the equalization fee, the allotment, the debenture, etc., must be studied by the Farm Bureau membership approximately five years before definite approval is given."[8] The initiative in the making of policies usually came from "the American" rather than from the grass roots, but the directors could not dictate to or drive their members. The process was one of government by consent—of persuasion rather than coercion—for in the last analysis the power of the Farm Bureau depended upon its ability "to deliver the vote" in state and federal government elections.

The A.F.B.F. has therefore not been the Farm Bureau. The essence of the Farm Bureau movement has been found in state and local organizations, and these have always varied enormously from state to state and even sometimes from county to county. The federation has been continuously striving for a national program, but it has had to achieve this through only a loose organization. It has had to depend upon a tradition of loyalty built up over the years, and upon consent to a program which has been hammered out of tough-minded recognition that it is to the interest of farmers to compromise their own differences in order to present a united front to opposing forces from without. Though the federation has sought ever since 1919, and particularly since McNary-Haugen days, for

[7] Grant McConnell, *The Decline of Agrarian Democracy* (Berkeley: University of California Press, 1953).

[8] A.F.B.F., "Report of the Washington Representative to the Board of Directors," *Minutes of the Board of Directors,* March 8-9, 1933.

a national agricultural program, it has equally insisted on decentralization of power in harmony with its own decentralized structure. Thereby it has found itself at times in a serious dilemma.

The state farm bureaus have varied widely in such crucial matters as membership dues, functions, and composition of membership. The A.F.B.F. has tried to encourage the states, with fair success, to keep membership dues high. But each state sets its own dues. During the period 1933-40, in Illinois, these were $15.00 per year. In Alabama, dues were $2.00. (By 1947, the prevailing rate in the Midwest and West was $10.00; in the Northeast and South, $5.00).[9] The only uniform requirement was that each state must pay to the federation 50 cents for each of its own paid-up members.

The tendency to keep dues high is probably related to the pattern of membership rise and decline. In times of prosperity, membership has expanded; in times of depression, declined—a pattern quite unlike that of preceding agrarian organizations which flourished as protest movements in times of depression (see Table 1). However, it is probably very much like the pattern of twentieth-century labor unionism, which has generally had much higher dues than the Farm Bureau, and which also has waxed strong in times of prosperity.

Some state farm bureaus have been particularly successful in certain activities, some in others. Illinois achieved outstanding success in the performance of three functions. The Illinois Agricultural Association early built up profitable "service organizations," such as automobile insurance and farm supply co-operatives; it has worked closely on agricultural education through a legal tie-up with the county agent system; and it has been very influential in the Illinois legislature on agricultural questions.

In New York state, the Farm Bureau has separated the three functions—education, legislation, and co-operative business enterprise. In New York, the emphasis of the Farm Bureau has always been on agricultural education, in co-operation with Cornell University and with the county agents. Co-operative or business activities of farmers in New York have been carried out through the Grange League Federation, composed of representatives of the Grange, the Dairymen's League, and the state Farm Bureau. Legislative policy (influencing the state legislature) has been carried out through the Legislative Board, which represented the same three organizations as the G.L.F.

---

[9] Kile, *op. cit.*, pp. 369-70.

The Ohio Farm Bureau was noted for its emphasis on serving the farmers as consumers, its extraordinarily successful insurance program being particularly outstanding. Participation in the Ohio Farm Bureau's insurance program was not confined to Farm Bureau members, but a percentage of the profits was retained for financing other Farm Bureau activities. Illinois returned all the profits of the "service organizations," except those kept for reserves, to the members of those organizations in the form of patronage dividends, and depended on the $15.00 I.A.A. membership fee to finance the state farm bureau's educational and legislative program. Nevertheless, the service organizations have been important membership builders in Illinois, for a farmer who saved over $15.00 per year in automobile insurance alone, through belonging to an organization affiliated with the I.A.A., was not likely to begrudge the I.A.A. membership fee. In fact, the chief difficulty has been to keep non-farmers out—for which purpose Illinois has tried to limit non-farmer (associate) members to 10 per cent, in order to keep the I.A.A. a farmers' organization.

The Alabama Farm Bureau gave up co-operative marketing organizations after the disastrous experience of sponsoring a cotton marketing co-operative which went bankrupt in 1931, amid charges of embezzlement against its board of directors.[10] It was not until the mid-forties that the Alabama Farm Bureau was able to overcome this history sufficiently to begin establishing farm supply and insurance co-operatives (automobile, life, and hospital insurance). The legislative influence of the Alabama Farm Bureau has been very strong. The Farm Bureau in fact dominated the Alabama legislature at times, while sometimes fighting the chief executive of the state. (Governor Jim Folsom was a latter-day object of Farm Bureau hostility.) Although, unlike Illinois and New York, there has been no legal tie with the Extension Service in Alabama, the relationship between the two organizations has been so close that it is hard to tell whether the Farm Bureau was promoting education and legislation through the Extension Service, or the Extension Service was promoting these activities through the Farm Bureau. There was a time when the Extension Service in Alabama dominated the Farm Bureau and was charged with being a political machine which elected not only the legislature but the governor (Bib Graves).

The degree to which the Farm Bureau has helped to fulfill the

---

[10] O'Neal to Captain E. L. Deal, Secretary of the Alabama Farm Bureau, May 28, 1931.

social needs of rural communities varies from state to state, and even from community to community. Community farm bureaus have been particularly active in Iowa. The allocation of membership dues in Iowa demonstrates the local emphasis in the Farm Bureau program of that state. In 1938, 90 out of 100 counties had raised their dues from $5.00 to $10.00 and these dues were allocated: $6.00 to be used in county farm bureau activities; $3.50 to the state organization; and 50 cents to the A.F.B.F.[11]

The Southern states, usually with lower membership dues than the Midwest, have not had so much money to support local programs, and have been more inclined to keep their eyes on political activities in Washington.

A "states-rights" doctrine with regard to its own organization has provided a definite check on the power of the national federation. The American federation has had little control over state and local membership policies other than to require that 50 cents per member be turned over to the A.F.B.F. While the states were supposed to report membership and dues once per month to the A.F.B.F., which had the technical right to audit their books, President O'Neal remarked: "The American Farm Bureau has a right to go back and audit the states' books but we might get shot if we do."[12] Mr. Yeager, a board member, confirmed this view by adding: "Now if we carry that out, it would be like taking your authority and investigating the various state Farm Bureaus and you will be run out."[13] When the Texas and Utah farm bureaus embarked on membership policies of which the A.F.B.F. did not approve, that is, collecting the membership dues through a check-off against the Farm Bureau co-operatives, the board could only agree with Director Blackburn: "They are out on an experiment and I don't know that there is anything we can do to change their attitude . . . you have got to let them carry through their experiment with the hope they will change.[14]

In interstate Farm Bureau relations, the A.F.B.F. has tried to act as mediator in conflicts, but has not been able to issue orders. Problems of this nature have been especially likely to arise in connection

---

[11] V. B. Hamilton, Secretary of the Iowa Farm Bureau, "Address to the Midwest Farm Bureau Training School, July 21, 1938," in "Minutes of the Midwest Training School, Lafayette, Indiana, July 17-21, 1938," A.F.B.F. regional files, folder marked "R. W. Blackburn."

[12] A.F.B.F., *Minutes of the Board of Directors,* December 14, 1934.

[13] *Ibid.*

[14] *Ibid.*

with state farm bureau insurance companies, some of which operated also in other states in competition with the farm bureau insurance companies of those states or with the State Mutual (known as Mr. Mecherle's company, a private insurance company which sometimes operated by agreement with state farm bureaus). In a discussion of this matter in 1933, Mr. Settle (director from Indiana) pointed out "that this was not a matter for the American Farm Bureau to decide; that the state Farm Bureau's business is not the American Farm Bureau's business and that if the American messed with it, we would get into deep water right away."[15] In 1934 the suggestion was made that the A.F.B.F. might overcome this difficulty by establishing an insurance company. To this Legal Counsel Kirkpatrick replied: "There is no legal reason, but it is a very delicate question and some have felt it was so largely a states-rights matter that it might look as though the American were an interloper."[16]

As has been previously stated, discipline of the states even on national policies adopted by majority vote of the A.F.B.F. was always dependent on the strong tradition of loyalty built up among the older members, and on the realization that self-interest demanded that a compromise agreed upon within the organization must be publicly supported outside. All the same, within the organization there might still be disagreement over it and efforts to change it. A state organization might without imputation of disloyalty openly oppose resolutions of the A.F.B.F. on policies other than those composing that central group known as "the farm program." For instance, the California Farm Bureau always used its influence to fight the reciprocal trade program even after the A.F.B.F. had adopted resolutions favoring it. Even on the major policy of the organization, if a state or a section refused to agree to the compromise, and believed its own major interests to be damaged thereby, it felt free to refuse to support or even to fight that policy, while still working with the majority on other policies. The Northeast was always opposed to production control, even when this was the central policy of the American federation's program, as it was during O'Neal's administration. Upon being asked by the federation in 1936 to send telegrams to Congress to support the Jones bill, New York replied that this would not be advisable, for New York farmers looked upon the Jones bill as a measure for crop control under the guise of conserva-

---

[15] *Ibid.*, December 7-8, 1933.
[16] *Ibid.*, December 14, 1934.

tion.[17] Massachusetts went further to say that any telegrams sent would be adverse to the passage of the bill.[18] The grand old man of the New York Farm Bureau, Howard E. Babcock, stated the gist of the states-rights doctrine thus: "The American Farm Bureau Federation has never spoken for New York in all matters."[19] When the Northeast was on the verge of revolting from the national federation on account of the A.F.B.F.'s support of the Agricultural Adjustment Administration, O'Neal reassured them by asserting his belief in states rights.[20]

An outstanding example of independent action by a state farm bureau is the testimony of the Ohio Farm Bureau at a Congressional hearing, in support of the Farm Security Administration, at the same time that the A.F.B.F. was working through Congress to fight the F.S.A.

Yet in spite of loose formal discipline, the unity achieved by the A.F.B.F. in the years 1933-40 is probably its most remarkable achievement. Basically it was founded on the realization that the members, as farmer producers, had more in common than in conflict, and that self-interest demanded they compromise their conflicts if they were to win any major concessions in the struggle with competing interest groups. But farmers had been divided ever since the Civil War, in spite of this basic truth. It still required leadership and strategy of a high order to unite them, for cohesion has been the exception rather than the rule among farmers.

The key question as to the democratic, or undemocratic, character of the A.F.B.F. is not what is the system of representation, but *whom* does it represent?

From its inception, the Farm Bureau has been a general farm organization, as have also the Grange and the Farmers' Union. That is, it has never considered itself a "commodity organization" and in fact has been opposed in principle to the existence of separate commodity co-operatives. This position has been adopted not so much because such co-operatives have threatened its own existence as because Farm Bureau leaders believed that a commodity organization (e.g., a cotton co-operative) would seek special privileges for its own commodity to the detriment or even the sacrifice of the

[17] Herbert P. King, President of the New York Farm Bureau, to O'Neal, February 20, 1936. This is probably a reference to the Bankhead-Jones bill, which became the Soil Conservation and Domestic Allotment Act of 1936.

[18] Howard S. Russell, Secretary of the Massachusetts Farm Bureau, to O'Neal, February 20, 1936.

[19] Babcock, personal interview, March 21, 1949.

[20] A.F.B.F., *Minutes of the Board of Directors,* June 20-22, 1934.

general farm program. Since the A.F.B.F. has long undertaken as one of its major tasks the compromising of conflicts among commodity interests in order to achieve agreement on a national farm program, naturally it has held that commodity interests should be represented within a general farm organization like the Farm Bureau. However, the description of the sectional alliance within the A.F.B.F. during the period of the New Deal and under the leadership of Edward O'Neal and Earl Smith as representing "the marriage of corn and cotton,"[21] while exaggerated, does point up the undeniable fact that the Farm Bureau was not entirely free from the taint of commodityism itself. Commodityism was inescapable in an organization based on a sectional alliance between Midwest and South, when corn was king in the one as cotton was in the other.

Thus the A.F.B.F. claimed to represent all commodities, and it was generally recognized that its scope was wider than that of any other national farm organization. This is one major reason why the U.S. Department of Agriculture chose to work so closely with it during the early period of the New Deal.[22] The other two general farm organizations, the Grange and the Farmers' Union, were too localized or too weak.

In addition to the three general farm organizations, there were two other groups which made up the "Big Five" of American agriculture, but these two, the Co-op Council and the Milk Producers' Federation, were generally considered to represent special commodity interests.

The question of *what farmers* the Farm Bureau represented is a little different. There have even been allegations that the Farm Bureau did not represent farmers at all.

The A.F.B.F. has been a genuine farmers' organization, though whether it has represented all classes of farmers, as it claims, is another matter. An amendment to the bylaws, passed in 1934, requires that all voting delegates to the annual meeting shall be "actual bona-fide farmers," a term which is not defined.[23] The officers of the Illinois Agricultural Association must be operating farmers, which means that they cannot be landlords alone. Even the president of the I.A.A., with headquarters in Chicago, consequently has had to go home to operate his farm on weekends.[24] While this re-

---

[21] "The Farm Bureau," *Fortune*, June, 1944, pp. 156 ff.

[22] Henry A. Wallace, personal interview, August 27, 1959.

[23] A.F.B.F., *Minutes of the Board of Directors*, December 8, 1934.

[24] Charles Shuman, then President of the I.A.A., personal interview, July 25, 1949.

quirement of the president of a several-million-dollar organization is something of a farce, still it has meant that he has had to keep in personal touch with the local farming situation.

Illinois tried to limit associate (non-farmer) members to 10 per cent though some counties in 1948 had as high as 24 per cent associate members.[25] In Alabama also, the state organization tried to limit associate members to 10 per cent, but recognized that local solicitors with a quota of members to get might find it easier to sign up a man on the sidewalks in town than to go out in the country to hunt up a farmer. No definition was made of "farmer" in Alabama —landlords, owner operators, and tenants all were eligible, and there was no way of checking whether a member actually was a farmer or not.[26]

While farmers are an economic group, it would be a mistake to attempt to analyze the composition of the membership of the Farm Bureau solely on the basis of economic criteria. It seems likely that there has been considerable correlation between educational level and Farm Bureau membership, for the Farm Bureau's origin in association with an educational movement has had lasting influence. The attraction between the county agent and the more progressive farmer was mutual. Evidence to support such an assumption is not readily available, however. All of the members of the first board of directors of the A.F.B.F. were said to be college-educated men, and some of them were members of the boards of trustees of their state land-grant colleges.[27]

It is fairly obvious that the A.F.B.F. did not represent all groups of farmers. A minority group like Negro farmers, for instance, was not likely to be very well represented. Since the state federations set their own membership policies, the American federation had no control over whether they admitted Negro members or not. Alabama did;[28] Louisiana did not.[29] Whether Negro members were admitted to all the responsibilities and privileges of membership also depended upon the local situation. O'Neal, with a paternalistic in-

---

[25] Notes made by the author at an I.A.A. meeting, November 15-18, 1948.

[26] Walter Randolph, President of the Alabama Farm Bureau, personal interview, May 26-27, 1949.

[27] James R. Howard, personal interview, June 22-23, 1949. Howard, first president of the A.F.B.F., held a bachelor's degree in philosophy from the University of Chicago.

[28] James L. Lawson, Supervisor of the Co-operative Extension Service, Auburn, Alabama, to O'Neal, March 24, 1937.

[29] A.F.B.F., *Minutes of the Board of Directors*, March 1-2, 1934.

terest, encouraged and wished to build up Negro membership in the
South.[30] In answer to an inquiry from him, R. G. Arnold, Organization Director of the Southern Region, estimated in 1939 that there
were 15,000 Negro members in the South, but said that no accurate
list was possible, as separate lists of white and Negro were not
kept.[31] A veteran county agent in Alabama, who had helped over
many years to build up the Farm Bureau and had succeeded against
considerable opposition in encouraging Negro membership, put the
matter succinctly: "We would rather have them join the Farm Bureau than the Farmers' Union."

A temporary split in the Alabama Farm Bureau in 1937 reveals
something of the status of Negro members. The basic cause of the
split had nothing to do with Negro membership (it was, in fact, the
result of dissension within the state Extension Service), but among
the charges and countercharges were some concerning Negro membership. The faction which withdrew from the state Farm Bureau
to form the Alabama Agricultural Association consisted chiefly of
the 21 counties of the black belt section. It maintained that while in
the Farm Bureau, it had two-thirds of the members, but had been
outvoted by the other two sections because representation was on
a county basis. The opposition's reply was that the membership in
the 21 counties had paid dues for colored members, and that the
colored members had never heard of the Farm Bureau.[32] The "peace
committee" which was established to restore harmony consisted of
representatives of the state Farm Bureau, of the Alabama Agricultural Association, and of the state Extension Service. It agreed to
recommend: "That state membership in farm organization [*sic*] be
based upon white members. Each county being permitted to handle
the colored membership as it thinks best."[33]

In Alabama, the state Farm Bureau federation took the lead in
organizing some conferences attended by both white and Negro
farmers, but these did not always work out successfully. In one such
conference arranged in Montgomery, the meetings were held in
hotels which would not accept Negroes except in small groups. It
was therefore arranged that the Negroes should meet in a Negro

[30] O'Neal's interest in Negro membership is attested by numerous letters in
the A.F.B.F. files.
[31] Arnold to O'Neal, January 13, 1939.
[32] *Montgomery Advertiser,* September 9, 1937.
[33] P. O. Davis, Director of the Alabama Extension Service and head of the
"peace committee," to O'Neal, R. K. Greene, and Judge F. M. Hare, December
31, 1937.

college in town. Some of them angrily protested, saying that they were dairy farmers and asking why they could not attend the dairy conference.[34] There is some indication that the state Farm Bureau had more success in holding such conferences in Birmingham, Alabama, rather than in Montgomery.

Usually the two races held separate Farm Bureau meetings in Alabama, though some meetings were held, all in courthouses, with white people seated on one side of the room and Negroes on the other. The state federation encouraged Negro membership, but did not have much to say as to how it should be handled. This was ordinarily left to the counties to decide.[35] It is quite probable that counties would have resented interference from the state federation on this matter as much as the states would have resented interference from the national federation.

One of the most indisputable facts about the A.F.B.F. is that it represented primarily the interests of commercial farmers—that is, those who depended upon the sale of farm products.[36] This is obvious from its policies, which were chiefly concerned with prices. Since price policy has comparatively little effect on subsistence or noncommercial farmers of whatever sort, or even on those commercial farmers whose resources are too small to enable them to make an acceptable living from farming even when prices are good, the Farm Bureau's major policies could not solve their problems. The Farm Bureau's rural welfare policies—such as support of federal aid to education, of state and local improvement of educational opportunities, and of rural hospital and medical care—may have touched the noncommercial farmers, but these usually have been

---

[34] Walter Randolph, personal interview, May 26-27, 1949. Randolph became president of the Alabama Farm Bureau in 1940.

[35] *Ibid.*

[36] There have been various precise definitions of the term "commercial farmer." The best way to arrive at a definition of a commercial farm is probably by defining "noncommercial" farms, and subtracting these from the total number. The definition below is the one depended upon here. It is from Jackson V. McElveen, *Family Farms in a Changing Economy,* U.S. Department of Agriculture, Agriculture Information Bulletin No. 171 (Washington: Government Printing Office, March, 1957), p. 1. "Non-commercial farms, as defined in this analysis of trends [says McElveen] are composed of *part-time* and *residential* farms and *subsistence* farms. Part-time and residential farms are those farms with total farm sales of less than $2,500 where the major source of money income or employment is from off-farm sources. Subsistence farms are those on which farm sales of less than $250 are the major source of cash income of the farm family." This definition is the one used in the 1954 census. For an earlier period adjustments have to be made, of course, to take account of price changes.

secondary even though important Farm Bureau policies. (The Associated Women have been the chief supporters of this type of policy.)

In 1930, commercial farms comprised 75 per cent of all farms enumerated in the census. In 1950 they constituted 65 per cent, but the decline in the proportion of commercial farms reflects not so much a trend to subsistence farming as a consolidation of commercial units, and an increase in part-time and residential farms.[37]

Commercial farms were not, however, necessarily or typically large-scale. One of the most striking characteristics of American agriculture has been the persistence of the relatively small-scale unit as the predominant type. In 1930 only 4.3 per cent of commercial farms were large-scale, and in 1954 the percentage was still the same.[38] (Large-scale farms were classified as those with incomes of $25,000 or more, using 1954 price levels.[39] Relative to business enterprises, even most of these would be very small indeed.)

Since family-size farms have constituted the bulk of American commercial agriculture, it is chiefly from this group that the American Farm Bureau has drawn its strength. In 1930, 95.7 per cent of all commercial agriculture was carried on by family-scale farms.[40] The percentage remained very much the same through the New Deal period, and in fact into the 1950's.[41]

It is probably true that the more prosperous family farmers have been the most likely to join the Farm Bureau. High membership fees, in most cases, would tend to keep others out. It was this type of substantial commercial family farmer that Earl Smith wished to attract. He believed that anyone in the United States worthy of the name "producing farmer" in 1934 could afford a ten-dollar membership fee,[42] and to the suggestion in 1933 that mortgaged farmers could not afford high membership fees his reply was that half the farms in Illinois were not mortgaged.[43]

As to the actual composition of the membership of the A.F.B.F., there are very few statistics that are of any value at all, except those

---

[37] *Ibid.*

[38] *Ibid.*, Table 19, p. 50.

[39] *Ibid.*

[40]*Ibid.*, Table 24, p. 72. The attempt to arrive at a precise definition of the term "family farm" has, however, generated more disagreement and considerably more heat, because of its emotional content, than even the term "commercial farm."

[41] *Ibid.*

[42] A.F.B.F., *Minutes of the Board of Directors,* March 1-2, 1934.

[43] *Ibid.*, August 16-17, 1933.

relating to total numbers. This is primarily because each state federation customarily set its own membership policies, and these varied enormously from state to state.

The regional membership figures give the best lead as to where the strength of Farm Bureau membership lay. In 1933, membership figures were: Midwestern, 98,292; Southern, 9,473; Western, 18,939; and Northeastern, 36,542.[44] Thus, at the beginning of the New Deal period considerably more than half of the membership of the Farm Bureau was located in one region—the Midwest.

Most Midwestern members of the Farm Bureau were family farmers, though family farmers of the upper income groups.[45] They were the salt-of-the-earth type, God-fearing, self-respecting, hard-working, and usually contented with their lot, which was ordinarily a prosperous one. It is hardly necessary to add that they were congenital Republicans. Coming from an area of contentment, it required a considerable spur to move them to adopt unconventional policies, farm or otherwise.

In contrast, the area of strength of the Farmers' Union was in the Great Plains, the very heart region of agrarian discontent. Not that the members of the Farmers' Union were smaller farmers than the ordinary members of the Farm Bureau. Indeed, a *Fortune* magazine survey in 1943 showed that the Farmers' Union, which claimed to represent "working farmers" and whose policies have, in fact, been often further to the left than those of the Farm Bureau, actually was composed almost entirely of farmers from the upper income level.[46] But they lived in a more unstable environment, and therefore they were more likely to favor radical solutions to problems. They were hurt more often, and when hurt would react more quickly and in a more extreme fashion.

Farm Bureau members were slower to move. But the circumstances of the Great Depression of 1929-33, which had been preceded by a prolonged farm depression, provided the spur (or the "burr under the tail," to use the expression of a well-known agricul-

---

[44] "Memberships Paid to the American Farm Bureau Federation," compiled by Dorothy Davis, Assistant Director of Information, A.F.B.F.

[45] This is the conclusion of the author. It was also stated to the author explicitly by Henry A. Wallace, personal interview, August 27, 1959. For a polemical statement of another point of view (that the Farm Bureau has been hostile to family-scale farms), see Dale Kramer, *The Truth About the Farm Bureau* (Falls Church, Virginia: National Affairs Press, 1950). Kramer was associated with the Farm Holiday movement and the Farmers' Union.

[46] "The Fortune Survey: Farmers II," *Fortune*, April, 1943, p. 8. The survey was carried out by the firm of Elmo Roper.

tural statesman). Their espousal of McNary-Haugenism was considered by the Harding-Coolidge-Hoover triumvirate to be a recrudescence of the most lawless frontier spirit.[47] Their support of Roosevelt's early New Deal program for agriculture was part of this genuine, though belated, agrarian rebellion. Its essence, like most agrarian rebellions in the American tradition and like the New Deal itself, was conservative, for it sought to preserve free American farmers from a descent into a European-like peasantry. At least that is the way it looked to Farm Bureau members. By 1932 even farmers who were usually prosperous were in desperate straits as they faced the likelihood of the loss of their farms through mortgage foreclosures.

---

[47] The various McNary-Haugen bills constituted the chief proposals for farm relief in the 1920's. They evolved out of the proposals of George N. Peek for a "fair-exchange value" for farm products — that is, a price which would restore the farmers' terms of trade (or the ratio of prices farmers received to the prices they paid) to what they had been just prior to World War I. Essentially, the McNary-Haugen proposals comprised a two-price system, with a higher "American" price for the domestically consumed portion of the crop, while the remainder of the crop was to be sold abroad at whatever price it would bring. Various plans for financing the scheme were proposed, the last one involving an "equalization fee" which was to be assessed on each unit of the farm commodity sold.

CHAPTER III

The Formation of the Sectional Alliance
Between the Midwest and the South

Sectional conflict and compromise are recurrent themes in Farm Bureau history. Even in the meetings called in 1919 and 1920 for the purpose of forming a national federation, there was manifest a painful cleavage between the Midwest and the Northeast which threatened the movement for a national organization. Since these two regions were the strongholds of the Farm Bureau, it was possible to establish the A.F.B.F. only by bridging over the conflict between them, although the breach was never entirely mended.

According to the views of both Howard E. Babcock[1] of the Northeast and James R. Howard[2] of the Midwest, the basic difference stemmed from the desire of the Northeast, on the one hand, to continue the original Farm Bureau emphasis on the educational approach to farm problems through co-operation with the Extension Service, and the insistence of the Midwest, on the other, that the time had come to make the direct economic (sometimes called the business) approach the predominant policy. The educational approach had meant teaching farmers how to raise their production through more efficient methods. In 1919, to the Midwest, the economic approach meant action by farmers to get higher prices for their crops, through eliminating "unfair marketing practices." As Northeastern dairy and poultry farmers were important buyers of Midwestern corn, they were not anxious to put the emphasis of the federation on raising crop prices. In contrast, Midwestern farmers

---

[1] Babcock, personal interview, March 21, 1949. Mr. Babcock, representing the New York Farm Bureau in 1919, sent out the call for the meeting to organize the A.F.B.F. He became an outstanding figure in farm organization circles in the Northeast.

[2] Howard, "Memoirs"; also personal interview, June 22-23, 1949.

were not enthusiastic for further education in the efficient production of crops if the benefits were passed on to other farmers in the form of lower prices for feedstuffs.

Howard believed there were even some Midwestern farmers who wished to break the tie with the Extension Service altogether. This extreme stand was opposed by him. At the permanent organization meeting in March, 1920, Henry C. Wallace, as guest speaker, succinctly expressed the dominant Midwestern point of view: "Now, people, if the purpose of this organization is to carry on the sort of work which the Farm Bureaus have been doing heretofore, which is for the purpose of education, for the purpose of stimulating production, the general line of work that has been carried on, then the Farm Bureau organization as you have started it now will serve no great useful purpose; in fact, it will do harm. But if this is anything at all, it is a business organization, to secure economic justice for the farmers."[3]

Dispute over representation on the board of directors arose in the permanent organization meeting of March 3-4, 1920, not 24 hours after the constitution had been adopted. The Midwest supported an amendment to abolish regional representation on the board of directors (then called the executive committee) in favor of election at large, arguing that since the Mississippi Valley constituted 65 per cent of the membership and paid 65 per cent of the finances of the A.F.B.F., democratic practice required that it should have commensurate representation.[4] One spokesman even mentioned "representation according to taxation." But the Northeast and the far West made clear that if regional representation were given up, they would no longer consider the A.F.B.F. a national organization. A New York delegate declared that the original purpose of regional representation "was to prevent at any time the control of this organization, which we concede is a national organization, falling into the hands of any one section or any one clique." He continued: "Now what we want is an organization which will speak for America, and you cannot get that if you put the control of that organization in one section."[5] A Californian added: "I think no harm is being done to have representation come from a little further [*sic*] and remote region than the Mississippi Valley."[6] The amendment was defeated.

---

[3] A.F.B.F., *Minutes of the Annual Meeting* (organization meeting), March 3-4, 1920, p. 224.

[4] *Ibid.*, pp. 190-200.

[5] *Ibid.*

[6] *Ibid.*

Although the Midwest did not gain the increased representation which it desired, it is fairly clear that its point of view predominated in the new national federation, for neither then nor subsequently was the primary emphasis of the A.F.B.F. placed on education. However, sufficient compromise—or rather, tolerance—of conflicting points of view was achieved to permit the glossing over of sectional differences in the formation of a national federation.

That the A.F.B.F. continued to be clearly aware of the political necessity of sectional compromise is demonstrated by a discussion at the annual convention in 1933. Here the Midwest group put forward a motion to increase representation at the annual convention by granting an extra voting delegate (in addition to the ones allotted each state) for every 5,000 paid-up memberships or major portion thereof, instead of the existing requirement of 20,000 memberships or major portion thereof. The argument for the motion was again that the Midwest was under-represented, and that states contributing only 10 per cent of the finances of the A.F.B.F. controlled the organization.[7] A delegate from New Jersey, opposing the amendment, pointed out the facts that each of the smaller states has two representatives in the United States Senate (the same as the Midwestern states have), that destroying the influence of these smaller states in the A.F.B.F. would cause the loss of their influence on the Senate, and that consequently the Midwest had to be saved from itself. A Midwesterner replied that there is another house of Congress in which the larger states have larger representation. A Nevada delegate declared that if such an amendment were passed, the far West would feel that it was not represented at all, and that there would no longer be an *American* Farm Bureau Federation. The motion was not passed.

That this was not a conflict between small and large states but rather a regional conflict is demonstrated by the fact that New York state, second to Illinois in terms of membership, stood with the small Northeastern states in opposition to the amendment. California, which also would gain in representation by the amendment, supported the far West in opposing it.[8]

James R. Howard was a Midwesterner, as have been all the other presidents of the A.F.B.F. since, with the sole and notable exception of Edward A. O'Neal, a Southerner. In accordance with the Midwestern emphasis on the business approach to farm problems, in the early years of the A.F.B.F. attempts were made to counter the pow-

---

[7] *Ibid.*, December 11-13, 1933, pp. 389-406.
[8] *Ibid.*

er of business monopolies by organizing the co-operative marketing, on a national scale, of five major types of farm products—grain, livestock, wool, cotton, and fruits and vegetables.

Some additional co-ordination of dairy products was also attempted. Aaron Sapiro of California was looked upon at this time as the leading authority on co-operative marketing, and he was prominent in national Farm Bureau activities because of his plan for compulsory pooling of crops through tying up all growers with iron-clad contracts. Later he was blamed by some Farm Bureau leaders as the disruptive element in the Farm Bureau co-operative movement.[9]

From the very beginning, however, the securing or influencing of legislation was understood to be one of the functions of the A.F.B.F., and soon this function became paramount. Co-operative marketing, it was found, could not succeed without support or at least legalization by the federal government, nor without the curbing and regulating of organized business antagonists. Even agricultural education required legislation to ensure the continuance and expansion of public appropriations on federal, state, and often even on county levels. When the A.F.B.F. decided to establish its Washington office in 1920, the Chamber of Commerce offered to take the Farm Bureau's staff into their building, as did other organizations which wished to capture the farmers' movement. Howard contemplated asking the Washington representative of the Grange, with which organization the Farm Bureau was quite friendly, to represent the Farm Bureau. Instead, he decided to establish a separate office in order that the A.F.B.F. might pursue an independent policy, co-operating with other groups or opposing them on particular issues as interest and wisdom might dictate.[10]

The infant organization was soon playing a significant role in Washington, for in 1921 the Senate Farm Bloc was formed in its offices. Accounts of the formation and functioning of the Farm Bloc have been given both by Howard[11] of the Farm Bureau and by Senator Capper[12] of Kansas, one of the leaders and original members of the bloc. They agree that it was formed in the A.F.B.F. offi-

[9] Howard, "Memoirs"; and personal interview, June 22-23, 1949.

[10] *Ibid.*

[11] James R. Howard, "Address to the Minnesota State Farm Bureau Federation, St. Paul, January 3, 1922," in Howard personal collection.

[12] Arthur Capper, "Address at the Annual Convention of the American Farm Bureau Federation, Chicago, Illinois, December 6, 1939," A.F.B.F., *Minutes of the Annual Meeting*, December 6, 1939 (paged separately); also Arthur Capper, *The Agricultural Bloc* (New York: Harcourt, Brace and Co., 192_), pp. 11-12.

ces on May 9, 1921. They also agree that membership was composed
about equally of senators from the Midwest and from the South.
Capper lists as the original members present in the office that day:
Senators W. S. Kenyon of Iowa, Arthur Capper of Kansas, George
W. Norris of Nebraska, F. R. Gooding of Idaho, E. F. Ladd of North
Dakota, Robert M. La Follette of Wisconsin, J. K. Kendrick of Wyo-
ming, E. D. Smith of South Carolina, Duncan U. Fletcher of Florida,
Joseph E. Ransdell of Louisiana, J. T. Heflin of Alabama, and Norris Sheppard of Texas. Howard confirms the statement that these
senators were present. Both Capper and Howard give some other
names, not necessarily of original members, Capper confirming all
the names listed by Howard, with one exception, and adding some
others.

The composition and function of the Farm Bloc is described by
Howard as follows:

The first meeting of the Senate agricultural bloc was held in the office
of the American Farm Bureau Federation in Washington, D.C., the
evening of May 9th. The Senators, known to be interested in the agricultural situation, were called by Senator William S. Kenyon of Iowa
and Gray Silver, Washington representative of the American Farm
Bureau Federation. Senator Kenyon told his colleagues that it was his
idea that by bringing together Senators from the Middle West and the
South, the principal agricultural sections, it would be possible to bring to
bear sufficient co-operative action in the Senate to enact legislative measures which would relieve agriculture. He also told the futility of his and
other Senators' endeavors to pass any kind of remedial or constructive
agricultural legislation during the previous short session of Congress.

Thus the agricultural bloc had its origin. It transcends party lines. It
has its own caucus and is not amendable [*sic*] to the party whip or party
discipline.

The agricultural bloc in the Senate is not sufficiently strong numerically
to pass legislation. The House bloc is proportionately weaker than the
Senate. Their strength lies in voting as a block and adding that strength
to one party or the other according to the way these parties favor or
oppose a measure. It is the principle of independent voting applied to
national legislation. It knows no party lines or political bosses.

The members are divided about equally between Democrats and Republicans, so it is truly bi-partisan. Most of the Westerners are Republicans and the Southerners are Democrats. In the Senate bloc the western
members all come from states west of Ohio. . . . The House block con-
tains members from as far east as Pennsylvania and is also bi-partisan in
make-up.[13]

Later on, in the New Deal period, farm bloc procedure was not
so simple and well disciplined. In fact there was no "Farm Bloc"

[13] Howard, "Address to the Minnesota Farm Bureau."

then, but there were many farm blocs—such as "Ed Smith's cotton bloc," Congressman Clarence Cannon's "little farm bloc," the "corn belt bloc," etc.—often co-existing, but with shifting composition over time.

The first period in the history of the A.F.B.F. came to an end in 1922, with the resignation of President Howard on account of tuberculosis. While the sectional alliance of farmers within the A.F.B.F. was primarily one of the Northeast and the Midwest, with the South as yet playing a very minor part, already the creation of the Farm Bloc, promoted by the Farm Bureau, represented an alliance *within Congress* of the two most important agricultural sections—the Midwest and the South.

The administration of Oscar E. Bradfute of Ohio, Howard's successor, was characterized by a predominant emphasis on co-operative marketing. Considerable opposition, however, developed within the Farm Bureau to Bradfute's program. In 1925 Edward A. O'Neal, then President of the Alabama Farm Bureau and member of the board of directors of the A.F.B.F., remarked that they had all had their troubles with fads and that after all, co-operative marketing was a fad of agriculture and that everybody had gotten crazy about it. He believed that they should "go back to the fundamentals" to get their bearings.[14] Another rising young leader, Earl C. Smith of Illinois, was deeply interested in promoting McNary-Haugenism, to which Bradfute was opposed.

By this time McNary-Haugenism had become a vital issue within the Farm Bureau, although the national federation had neither originated nor at first supported it. But after a time the A.F.B.F. came to play an extremely important part in the McNary-Haugen movement, as Clifford V. Gregory, editor of the *Prairie Farmer,* perceptively pointed out. The McNary-Haugen fight, says Gregory, was carried on by a Corn Belt Committee of Twenty-two, including Henry A. Wallace, George N. Peek, and Chester C. Davis. Its strongest support came from the A.F.B.F., which was able to swing states outside the corn belt into support.[15] Within a few years, the words Agricultural Adjustment Administration could almost be substituted for McNary-Haugen in this statement (if the words "Corn Belt Committee of Twenty-two" are deleted). Thus to a marked de-

---

[14] A.F.B.F., *Minutes of the Board of Directors,* April 23-24, 1925.

[15] Clifford V. Gregory, "The American Farm Bureau Federation and the A.A.A.," in Harwood L. Childs (ed.), *Pressure Groups and Propaganda* (Annals of the American Academy of Political and Social Science, Vol. CLXXIX [May, 1935]), p. 153.

gree in the McNary-Haugen movement, the A.F.B.F. was rehearsing the role it would play in the New Deal for agriculture.

The setting for the proposed McNary-Haugen legislation is to be found in the agricultural depression which had begun in 1920, when the purchasing power of farm products tumbled, then rose a bit in subsequent years, and dipped again in 1926. The basic research out of which McNary-Haugenism as well as the New Deal agricultural programs evolved was those studies of cost-price relationships carried on in government offices, particularly in the Department of Agriculture.[16] But the publicist extraordinary and inventor of mechanisms for McNary-Haugenism was undoubtedly George Peek.

The ideals on which the McNary-Haugen plan was based were set forth in the pamphlet *Equality for Agriculture*, written by George Peek and Hugh S. Johnson in 1922.[17] Peek claims to have been the originator, with Johnson as his assistant.[18] They talked with the first president of the A.F.B.F. about it, but Howard would not then commit himself to it. Later he came around to the view that it was the best thing in the circumstances.[19] The second president of the A.F.B.F., Bradfute, was typical of the old-guard prosperous farm leader to whom McNary-Haugenism appeared alarmingly like an attempt to rock the boat.

Meantime the Wallaces of Iowa had become active supporters of the Peek-Johnson scheme, which later became identified as McNary-Haugenism. In fact, Henry A. Wallace says that his father, then Secretary of Agriculture in the Harding administration, had the bill drawn up and subsequently persuaded McNary and Haugen to introduce it into Congress. Henry A. Wallace, then editor of *Wallace's Farmer*, was working actively behind the scenes to swing the Iowa Farm Bureau to support McNary-Haugenism.[20]

Over the opposition of the old guard, the Iowa Farm Bureau endorsed McNary-Haugenism. At about the same time, the Illinois

[16] For the evolution of "parity," see John D. Black, *Parity, Parity, Parity* (Cambridge, Massachusetts: The Harvard Committee on Research in the Social Sciences, 1942), Chap. 5.

[17] In James R. Howard's private collection there is a copy marked in Howard's handwriting: "Geo. Peek & Hugh Johnson. Original draft." Henry A. Wallace says that the authorship of *Equality for Agriculture* was unknown until the second edition appeared, addressed to Howard and bearing the names of the joint authors. See Henry A. Wallace, *New Frontiers* (New York: Reynal and Hitchcock, 1934), p. 145.

[18] Peek to O'Neal, May 16, 1943.

[19] Howard, "Memoirs"; and personal interview, June 22-23, 1949.

[20] Wallace, personal interview, August 27, 1959. Some of this account is also given in his *New Frontiers*, pp. 147-55.

Agricultural Association became a center of agitation in favor of this scheme, with George Peek and Chester Davis, his lieutenant, later using its offices as their headquarters.[21] William Hirth of Missouri also became a particularly strong proponent of McNary-Haugenism in the Midwest.[22]

McNary-Haugenism was a doctrine of extreme economic nationalism which made a strong appeal to the traditional pro-tariff leanings of the Midwestern farmer. At last Midwestern farmers were beginning to doubt the efficacy of the ordinary tariff as a means of raising farm prices. But Peek and Johnson pointed out that what was needed was not to surrender the tariff, but to close the breach in the protective tariff system by finding a way to secure equality for agriculture in its benefits.

Since Southern farmers were from a traditionally free trade or low tariff region, they were more slowly converted to McNary-Haugenism. After the principles of McNary-Haugenism did win support in the South, George Peek was always mystified as to how Southern farmers could, at the same time, cling to their belief in the virtues of a low tariff system.[23]

The first McNary-Haugen bill was defeated in the House of Representatives in 1924, and it was clear that a combination of Eastern and Southern votes was responsible for the failure. From that time a number of individuals began to work to cement the Midwestern and Southern farmers. One of these was Henry A. Wallace.[24] At the same time, and as a result of the same forces, the crucial sectional alliance between the Midwest and the South within the A.F.B.F. was formed.

Against the setting of endorsement of McNary-Haugenism by several powerful Midwestern state farm bureaus, the election of a new president of the A.F.B.F. took place at the annual convention, December 7-9, 1925. Conflict over policy within the American Farm Bureau became openly apparent in the three-cornered fight which took place for the presidency. The candidates were the incumbent, Oscar E. Bradfute of Ohio, whose platform was cooperative marketing; Sam H. Thompson of Illinois, with Earl Smith as his campaign manager, advocating McNary-Haugen legislation as a national farm program; and Edward A. O'Neal of Alabama, who was then primarily interested in the development of Muscle Shoals.

---

[21] Kile, *op. cit.*, p. 132.
[22] Wallace, *op. cit.*, pp. 158-59; and personal interview, August 27, 1959.
[23] Peek to O'Neal, November 14, 1941, and May 13, 1943.
[24] Wallace, personal interview, August 27, 1959.

The Northeastern delegates as well as Ohio favored Bradfute. The Midwest was for McNary-Haugenism. The South, weakest in membership but holding the balance of power, was not then committed on McNary-Haugenism. The vote on the first ballot stood: 18 for Thompson; 17 for Bradfute; 9 for O'Neal. Twenty-three votes were necessary for a majority. Ballot after ballot was taken with very little change in the voting. On the eighth ballot came a dramatic and decisive switch, the votes being: 24 for Thompson; 19 for Bradfute; and 1 for O'Neal. Sam H. Thompson of Illinois, the Midwestern candidate, thus was elected with the support of the South.[25] While there were no overt promises, it is apparent that an agreement had been made behind the scene. In return for Southern votes for Thompson (the representative of McNary-Haugenism), the Midwestern members would be willing to support the development of Muscle Shoals.[26] Furthermore, O'Neal was re-elected vice-president of the A.F.B.F. on the basis of Midwestern as well as Southern votes. Thus was cemented that alliance between Midwestern and Southern farmers that was destined to prove so potent in the days of the early New Deal.

An analysis of the votes in Congress on the various McNary-Haugen bills shows how important to the success of farm legislation was the Midwestern-Southern agrarian alliance. The American Farm Bureau leaders were quite conscious of this fact, for careful records were kept in the Farm Bureau headquarters of the votes *by sections* on the McNary-Haugen bills (see Table 2).[27] Not until 1927, when the Southern members joined their Midwestern colleagues, did the bill get through Congress. O'Neal himself, then the acknowledged leader of the Southern group in the A.F.B.F., was

---

[25] A.F.B.F., *Minutes of the Annual Meeting,* December 7-9, 1925, pp. 242-59.

[26] The site of a dam on the Tennessee River which eventually became one of the chief power sites of the Tennessee Valley Authority. At that time O'Neal was primarily concerned that the facilities at Muscle Shoals should be used to produce large quantities of fertilizer, and thus bring down the cost of fertilizer to farmers. In a time of low farm prices, the cost of fertilizer was an almost insupportable burden to Southern farmers, though it might be unimportant or even negligible on the more fertile Midwestern prairies.

[27] On the records in the A.F.B.F. there is also the notation that of those who were for the bill in 1927 in the Senate, 13 were from the South and 18 from the Midwest, or a total of 64 per cent of those who were for the bill; in the House, 76 were from the South and 103 from the Midwest, or a total of 84 per cent; in 1928, in the Senate, the figures were 20 Southerners and 19 Midwesterners, or 73 per cent; while the figures in the House were 72 Southerners and 94 Midwesterners, or 81 per cent.

TABLE 2

Congressional Voting on the McNary-Haugen Bills by Sections, 1924-28 [a]

House of Congress	Date	Action	Votes Cast		
			Section	For	Against
House	6/ 2/24	Defeated	South	22	84
			East	13	97
			Midwest	95	37
			West	24	6
			Totals	154	224
House	5/21/26	Defeated	South	41	69
			East	9	93
			Midwest	97	41
			West	20	9
			Totals	167	212
Senate	6/24/26	Defeated	South	8	16
			East	2	19
			Midwest	15	5
			West	14	5
			Totals	39	45
Senate	2/11/27	Passed	South	13	11
			East	3	17
			Midwest	18	5
			West	14	6
			Totals	48	39
House	2/17/27	Passed	South	76	43
			East	12	98
			Midwest	103	30
			West	22	7
			Totals	213	178
Senate	4/12/28	Passed	South	20	3
			East	2	15
			Midwest	19	1
			West	12	4
			Totals	53	23
House	5/ 3/28	Passed	South	72	29
			East	14	71
			Midwest	94	18
			West	24	3
			Totals	204	121

[a] Source: Statistics in A.F.B.F. research files.

said by old-timers on the A.F.B.F. staff not to have been enthusiastic for McNary-Haugenism until the price of cotton fell (from an average of 19.6 cents per pound in 1925 to an average of 12.5 cents in 1926).[28]

The fact that President Coolidge vetoed each McNary-Haugen bill that was successful in Congress led the Farm Bureau to turn its closest attention to Presidential elections. By 1927, in the eyes of the A.F.B.F., Congress was all right. The problem was to get a President who would be sympathetic.

The Midwestern Republican members of the Farm Bureau turned to Governor Frank O. Lowden of Illinois as their candidate. Earl Smith of Illinois was particularly active at the national convention on Lowden's behalf. Smith was spokesman for a group which presented their own agricultural plank to the convention. It was voted crashingly down by 806 to 278.[29] When Hoover was nominated, the official publication of the A.F.B.F. accused the Republican national convention of steam-roller tactics, and called Frank Lowden "the real martyr of 1928 politics." The resolutions committee of the convention, declared the *Bureau Farmer*, was packed by the machine, which prevented the opposition of Illinois, Iowa, Indiana, Missouri, Kansas, Oklahoma, Minnesota, Nebraska, the Dakotas, and West Virginia to Herbert Hoover from becoming effective. The senators and congressmen from Kansas, for example, were almost unanimously for a McNary-Haugen plank, but William Allen White, who was avowedly against the measure, was named as Kansas representative on the resolutions committee.[30] The fact that the Republican convention of 1928 turned down Earl Smith's proposals for a McNary-Haugen plank on farm policy was remembered by farmers in 1932—and it was still fresh in the mind of Earl Smith almost 20 years later.

The Democratic convention which chose Alfred E. Smith as its nominee gave a much more favorable reception to the platform advocated by the A.F.B.F. Henry A. Wallace says that he tried to persuade Lowden to come out for Al Smith, but in this he was unsuccessful.[31] In the election of 1928, Midwestern farmers clung to

---

[28] The price of cotton is from U.S. Bureau of the Census, *Historical Statistics of the United States, 1789-1945* (Washington: Government Printing Office, 1949), p. 108.

[29] William T. Hutchinson, *Lowden of Illinois* (2 vols.; Chicago: University of Chicago Press, 1957), II, 598-99.

[30] *Bureau Farmer* (Illinois ed.), July, 1928, pp. 13-14 (of the Illinois section).

[31] Wallace, personal interview, August 27, 1959.

their traditional allegiance to the Republican Party, in spite of its repudiation of their candidate.

Coolidge was the least co-operative of Presidents, from the Farm Bureau's point of view. While Hoover was not the Farm Bureau's candidate, and the Farm Bureau considered his plan to relieve agriculture through the establishment of the Federal Farm Board "was not our baby," still Farm Bureau leaders were optimistic that some good might come of it, and urged hearty co-operation with it. The hopefulness with which the A.F.B.F. greeted the enactment of the law establishing the Federal Farm Board was expressed by President Thompson: "The present bill will be amended. It is safe to predict that. No plan is perfect at first. The Board will make mistakes— it is human. But a great victory has been won; the nation has adopted a policy of equality for agriculture. Brighter days are ahead for the farm people of the United States."[32]

As President Thompson spoke these words in September, 1929, it is apparent that he, and probably other farmers, shared something of the optimistic boom psychology that preceded the crash in October. Thompson was himself appointed a member of the Federal Farm Board in 1931, a recognition of which the A.F.B.F. was quite proud.

The cautious optimism with which the creation of the Federal Farm Board had been greeted soon gave way to condemnation as agricultural prices plunged down farther and faster. The old cry for "balance" (which goes back to William Jennings Bryan and the election of 1896) was revived, and the new term "parity" was added. The *Bureau Farmer* for February, 1930, says: "A few years ago it was 'equality' for agriculture. Today we are seeking a 'parity' for agriculture. Different words but they mean the same thing."[33] In 1932 a resolution adopted at the annual meeting of the A.F.B.F. reads in part: "For years the American Farm Bureau Federation has urged the adoption of a national program to restore and maintain a *fair price parity* [italics mine] between that part of our staple cash crops consumed in this country and the goods and services farmers buy."[34]

Just as McNary-Haugenism was the chief symbol of Farm Bureau policy during the years 1925-31, under the administration of Presi-

[32] Sam H. Thompson, "The Battle for Equality," *Bureau Farmer* (Illinois ed.), September, 1929, p. 35.
[33] Editorial, *ibid.*, February, 1930, p. 6.
[34] A.F.B.F., *Resolutions of the Annual Meeting*, 1932,

dent Thompson, so "parity" became the symbol and slogan of the A.F.B.F. during the long presidency of O'Neal, who succeeded Thompson.

Actually the two symbols were very closely associated. George Peek maintained that he was the originator of both. Later he wrote to O'Neal: "You may have forgotten the fact that the idea of Parity (or as it was formerly expressed 'fair exchange value') between farm and industrial products originated with me and was developed with the assistance of General Johnson in the form of the brief, EQUAL-ITY FOR AGRICULTURE."[35] That "parity" is a lineal descendant of McNary-Haugenism is clear from O'Neal's terse explanation: "Parity payments are not subsidies. They are the farmer's tariff."[36]

When Thompson accepted President Hoover's invitation to become a member of the Federal Farm Board in 1931, O'Neal automatically stepped up from the vice-presidency to the presidency of the A.F.B.F. At the end of this term, O'Neal in his own right was elected president, with the support of Earl Smith. The membership of the South in the A.F.B.F. was still very weak, compared to that of both the Midwest and the Northeast, but political winds in the country at large were blowing Democratic. The fact that Hearst of Iowa was elected vice-president and that Earl Smith of Illinois (powerful as president of the Illinois Agricultural Association and experienced in Republican politics) supported O'Neal made it clear that the Midwestern-Southern alliance, cutting across both sectional and party lines, was firmly established.

Since these were the two most important agricultural sections, it was a much more powerful alliance than the original combination between the Midwest and Northeast had been. Apart from economic or political considerations, the harmonious relationship thus signi-fied has a place in social history. Since Civil War days, Midwestern and Southern farmers had been mutually suspicious and antagonistic. Even in the early days of the A.F.B.F. old-timers say that the South-ern "boys" at the annual convention used to meet separately from the Midwestern group and that each section viewed the other with suspicion that was a survival of the bitterness of Civil War and Re-construction. Gradually, as in the national organization they came to understand each other's problems as farmers, and as the leaders

---

[35] Peek to O'Neal, May 16, 1943.

[36] "Address of Edward A. O'Neal, June 20, 1939," in "Minutes of the West-ern Regional Conference, Santa Cruz, California, June 20, 1939," A.F.B.F. re-gional conference files. Probably this address was read by someone else, as O'Neal was unable to attend this conference.

came to know each other personally, the old suspicion gave way. To imply that all was harmony thereafter would be misleading, but whatever conflicts did occur between the Midwest and South were chiefly based on differences in interest, rather than on the emotions that were an aftermath of the Civil War. Time may have been the great healer, but the American Farm Bureau Federation helped.

CHAPTER IV

Ed O'Neal and the Inauguration of the
New Deal for Agriculture

The key to the desperate mood of farmers on the eve of the inauguration of Franklin D. Roosevelt is to be found not so much in statistics of farm prices as in the situation arising from rural mortgage
debts. The Farmers' Holiday movement dramatized these conditions
and made them concrete. The officers of the A.F.B.F. kept a wary
though not unsympathetic eye on the movement, and took pains to
keep themselves informed about it.[1]

While the A.F.B.F. was still calling for legislative action to aid
distressed farmers, the Farmers' Holiday movement in 1932 and
early 1933 called for direct action, in a manner that showed the influence both of modern labor unionism and traditional frontier ways.
The Holiday movement advised farmers to withhold their produce
from the market until a price equal to "cost of production" were
offered on the market. When enough farmers had joined the
movement, a general strike was to occur—that is, farmers were to
withhold their goods from the market, beginning at a date to be announced. Actually, instead of waiting for the general strike, a number of unauthorized, spontaneous strikes took place. In some areas,
direct action sponsored by the Farmers' Holiday associations took
the form of preventing the foreclosure of mortgages or the collection of taxes. Though not synonymous with the Farmers' Union,
Farmers' Union people such as Milo Reno and John Simpson were
prominent in its leadership, and the demand for "cost of production"

---

[1] In the files of the A.F.B.F. there is quite a collection of materials about
the Farmers' Holiday movement—newspaper clippings, letters from Farm
Bureau and Extension people, etc. O'Neal seemed to be interested in gaining
authentic information about it, probably as a basis for judgment as to whether
the Farm Bureau should take counteraction.

was a Farmers' Union slogan (in contrast with the Farm Bureau's demand for "parity" prices). The centers of the movement were in Iowa and Minnesota, with considerable activity also in South Dakota and Wisconsin, and some in Michigan and other Midwestern states. There appears to have been none south of the Ohio River.

After the first outburst of strikes, the Farmers' Holiday movement devoted itself largely to preventing the carrying out of mortgage foreclosures. These actions seem to have been associated with the Holiday movement, rather than sponsored by it. The center of radical agitation was northwestern Iowa, where martial law was declared in several counties (Plymouth and Crawford and one other) as a result of the direct action of the farmers to prevent the courts from carrying out mortgage foreclosures. The stories read like those of the Regulator Movement of Revolutionary days. A judge who refused to swear that he would not sign any more foreclosure actions was taken from his courtroom to a crossroads, and a warning noose was placed around his neck.[2] The attorney for an insurance company was threatened with hanging.[3] And in another case farmers clashed with troops who had been sent to supervise the sale of goods at a farm.[4]

Most typical of the frontier spirit were the "penny sales," in which farmers who had gathered to prevent strangers from bidding for the property of a neighbor which had been put up in forced sale for debt or taxes would themselves bid in the property for pennies, and then would return it to the original owner. A description of one such event at Mecosta, Michigan, is that of a chattel mortgage sale ordered to satisfy a $150 debt. Prices bid were such as three cents for a bean puller, ten cents for a grain drill, and five cents for a piano.

Farmer neighbors and their wives gathered—some 200 of them. No one bid more than 25¢ for anything offered. When the hammer had fallen for the last time, the bidders went home, leaving their purchases where they stood. The taxes totalled $150. Proceeds of the sale were $2.06. Loss to the creditor $147.94.

It was the first time in Michigan that farmers had come out to a forced sale, bid in the chattels for a song, and turned them over to the original owner. In recent weeks newspapers have been peppered with similar reports from Iowa, Wisconsin, Minnesota, Ohio, Pennsylvania, Oklahoma, the Dakotas, Nebraska, and other states. Sometimes the hint of force has prevented substantial bids.

Legal or not, this sort of answer to mortgage foreclosures and other

---

[2] *Sioux City Journal*, April 30, 1933.
[3] *Ibid.*
[4] *Ibid.*

forced sales has put on the brakes. Seldom has a community had more than one such sale, said a Wisconsin editor. The New York Life Insurance Co. announced its suspension of mortgage foreclosures in Iowa pending mortgage relief action by the Iowa legislature.[5]

Such actions died down whenever state legislatures passed mortgage moratorium laws, as for example Minnesota did. Moreover, when Roosevelt went into office in the spring of 1933, there was an attitude of watchful waiting on the part of farmers to see whether federal relief would be forthcoming. An informed estimate of the situation was made by Carl C. Taylor, who sat through the meeting of the National Farmers' Holiday Association in Des Moines on May 3 and 4, 1933, which was considering whether to call for a nationwide farmers' strike on May 13. Taylor said: "Whether the movement is gaining or losing I simply do not know. My own guess is that it is at its high point, that an attempt to carry through the strike on the eve of rising farm prices and the enactment of the Federal Farm Relief Bill, will put the Association in a bad light. I am inclined to think Reno thinks the same thing."[6]

That the Farmers' Holiday Association was hostile to the Farm Bureau there is no doubt. In Harrison County, Iowa, they had the Farm Bureau literally thrown out of the courthouse.[7] And in Iowa, where the Extension Service was tied to the Farm Bureau, they were also hostile to the county agents.[8] Such opposition to the county agents may have been in part an outcome of the demand for tax relief, for in Iowa the salaries of county agents were paid in part from county taxes. Whether the Farmers' Holiday movement was responsible for a loss of membership in the Farm Bureau in Iowa is questionable. The secretary of the A.F.B.F. wrote that the Holiday movement had caused them to lose half their members in one state, and it is clear that he meant Iowa. But some other Farm Bureau leaders believed that the loss in membership was associated with farmers' inability to pay membership dues in the depression, and that the Holiday movement may even have helped the Farm Bureau by dramatizing conditions and thus making farmers and the general public more willing to support the Farm Bureau's proposals for relief through legislation. President O'Neal wrote: "I am deeply

---

[5] *Michigan Farm News*, February 4, 1933, p. 1.

[6] Taylor, formerly dean of the graduate school at the North Carolina State College, who was at this time conducting a series of lectures in Des Moines, to H. R. Kibler, May 5, 1933, A.F.B.F. research files.

[7] Daisy Williams, Secretary-Treasurer of the Iowa Farm Bureau, to Kibler, April 17, 1933, *ibid.*

[8] H. M. Hayes, county agent, to Kibler, May 3, 1933, *ibid.*

sympathetic with the objectives sought by those who are sponsoring this movement. . . . However, it is my firm conviction that the methods followed in the present instance cannot result in general success. . . . I am convinced that the real solution of the farm problem lies not in a temporary strike, but in securing the establishment of a sound national agricultural policy."[9]

Especially interesting is the fact that a center of the Farmers' Holiday movement was in northwestern Iowa, an area of some of the richest farm lands in the world. While there was some attempt within the Farm Bureau on the part of opponents of the movement to attribute it to Communists, professional agitators, radical leaders, poor farmers, and unemployed, all available evidence points instead to the conclusion that it was a desperate effort on the part of property-owning farmers to prevent the loss of their property. Several people who were active in the Iowa Farm Bureau at the time and who witnessed some of the activities of the Holiday movement there agreed that it was a genuine farmers' movement whose participants were often conservative substantial farmers, normally regarded as pillars of the community, whom conditions had made desperate.[10]

Explanations as to why such a movement took place in so fertile a farming area are chiefly economic—especially a debt situation based on the inflated land values following World War I, as well as several years of drought and grasshoppers, in addition to low prices. Another explanation that has been offered has a cultural base— namely, that many farmers of that region were of German stock, conservative, good in business but without much experience in politics. While to this group "penny sales" seemed the answer to mortgage foreclosures, the Iowa Farm Bureau urged farmers to take advantage of all legal loopholes to keep their farms. The Farm Bureau also assisted in the setting up of the debt adjustment committees, provided for by the Iowa legislature, as a means of bringing about agreement between debtors and creditors.

There was at least one minor agrarian organization active in the Midwest and Great Plains during the early 1930's which was con-

---

[9] O'Neal to the presidents, secretaries, and boards of directors of the Iowa county farm bureaus, August 30, 1932, *ibid.*

[10] Allan B. Kline, personal interview, May 17, 1949; and Herman Aaberg (who was at that period a county agent in northwestern Iowa), personal interview, May 17, 1949. Many letters from Extension Service directors in the Midwest during this period (A.F.B.F. research files) express surprise at the number of leading farmers involved in the movement.

siderably more extreme. This was the United Farmers, which maintained that it represented "the poor and middle farmers." Its official publications carried the slogan "Workers of the World Unite," and called upon its members to vote Communist.[11] This organization too is indicative of the unrest and discontent prevalent in the richest part of agricultural America, but it seems to have had very little influence.

In contrast to such a truly radical organization, the primary aim of the Farmers' Holiday movement was the same as that of the A.F.B.F., namely, to raise farm product prices. The direct and often illegal methods associated with the Farmers' Holiday movement differed from the political means of obtaining farm relief proposed by the A.F.B.F. Yet the same agricultural depression which produced the Holiday associations was the basic soil out of which the program of the A.F.B.F. evolved in the early 1930's. More than likely it was O'Neal's knowledge of such activities as the "penny sales" of the Farmers' Holiday associations which led him to warn a Senate committee in January, 1933: "Unless something is done for the American farmer we will have revolution in the countryside within less than twelve months."[12]

The year 1932 was a time of flux and confusion among farm organization forces. McNary-Haugenism seemed dead as a political issue after Hoover rejected it in the election of 1928. Yet no single alternative program had anything like the clustered support or the crusading symbolism as a "measure of righteousness"[13] which McNary-Haugenism had commanded. The old agrarian stand-bys of trust-busting and currency reform, which had been largely superseded by the McNary-Haugen program, were still doggedly endorsed in the Farm Bureau's resolutions, but without much faith in their potency. Only the farmers of the conservative Northeast and of Ohio clung to the once-radical monetary program with undiminished faith and zeal. Professor George F. Warren of Cornell was still "the professor," held in the highest respect by the A.F.B.F., and his scheme for the "commodity dollar" was regularly endorsed.[14]

[11] *Producer's News* (official organ of the United Farmers' League in the Northwest; Plentywood, Montana), November 27, 1931; and *United Farmer* (official organ of the United Farmers' League affiliated with the Farmers' International; New York Mills, Minnesota), October 6, 1930.

[12] Quoted in Arthur M. Schlesinger, Jr., *The Coming of the New Deal* (Boston: Houghton Mifflin Co., 1959), p. 27.

[13] The phrase is Henry A. Wallace's.

[14] The commodity dollar was essentially a device for stabilizing the general price level.

However, there was apparently an uneasy feeling that the grand agrarian scheme for monetary reform would not be enough.

By 1932 "parity" was the accepted goal of Farm Bureau policy. This was nothing really new, however, for under the name "fair-exchange value" parity had been the main theme and goal of Mc-Nary-Haugenism. Professor George Warren's scheme for the "commodity dollar" was, in more direct line, descended from the old-time currency reformers, but there was an indirect connection through George Peek, between parity and the more traditional crusades for softening or stabilization of the currency. Peek had got the statistical basis for his idea of "fair-exchange value" from U.S. Department of Agriculture, Bulletin No. 999, *Prices of Farm Products in the United States,* published in 1921 and written by George Warren, the chief of the latter-day monetary reformers.[15]

In 1932 each of the three main farm organizations was identified with a different scheme for the salvation of agriculture—the Grange was still for the export debenture plan,[16] the Farmers' Union called for "cost of production," and the Farm Bureau wanted "parity" but was not quite sure how to get it. Once they even joined in supporting a bill, popularly known as the "three-headed monster," which contained the gist of all three schemes. In mid-1932, Earl Smith was responsible for the introduction into Congress of a bill sponsored by the Farm Bureau (the Rainey-Norbeck bill).[17] In Farm Bureau circles, the Democratic Speaker of the House, John Nance Garner, was blamed for the failure of this measure, the charge being that he would not permit the invoking of a special rule to bring it to a vote, as he wished to postpone agricultural legislation until the incoming Democratic administration could get the credit for it. Garner was not popular with the Farm Bureau either then or when he became Vice-President of the United States.

Meantime, the "voluntary domestic allotment plan" had gained considerable support.[18] Most prominently associated with the origin

---

[15] Black, *op. cit.,* p. 46.

[16] A plan proposed by Professor Charles L. Stewart of the University of Illinois as a means of achieving differential prices on domestic and foreign markets.

[17] This was an emergency bill to aid wheat, cotton, and hog producers for one year.

[18] While the general object of this plan was similar to that of the McNary-Haugen bills, it introduced one very important new feature. This was the assignment of specific allotments to individual growers, tied to some historical base. M. L. Wilson, John D. Black, and Mordecai Ezekiel were responsible for the formulation of the Hope-Norbeck bill of 1932, which embodied the "voluntary domestic allotment plan." Though not passed, this bill was the forerunner of the Agricultural Adjustment Act of 1933.

and early development of it were W. J. Spillman of the Department of Agriculture, Beardsley Ruml, then Director of the Laura Spellman Rockefeller Memorial Foundation, and John D. Black of Harvard University, who acted in a part-time capacity as adviser to the Federal Farm Board.[19] M. L. Wilson of Montana took up the domestic allotment plan, adding much that was creative, especially in the way of provision for voluntary grass-roots participation, and he became the great exponent of it.[20] It was the Wilson version which became known as the "voluntary domestic allotment plan."[21]

Wilson is a key figure in the early New Deal farm program, for he was in close touch with both the Administration and with the farm organizations.[22] He was deeply and emotionally involved, and yet he kept the balanced and detached point of view of a philosopher.[23] Apparently he exercised his gently persuasive influence effectively on Ed O'Neal, with whom he talked in 1932. He felt that O'Neal was groping for a policy to strengthen the rather weak resolutions of that year's annual meeting, and that he was in a receptive frame of mind.[24] When O'Neal later brought Wilson and Earl Smith together, Wilson found Smith harder to persuade. It appeared to Earl Smith that Wilson's proposed committees of farmers would constitute a possible rival organization to the Farm Bureau.[25]

As the Presidential campaign of 1932 gathered momentum, it became increasingly clear to farm organization leaders that Franklin D. Roosevelt would make the sympathetic President for whom they had been looking since Coolidge's first veto of the McNary-Haugen bill. In his acceptance speech, Democratic nominee Roosevelt had said that his party "stood ready to be guided by whatever the re-

---

[19] Theodore Saloutos and John D. Hicks, *Agricultural Discontent in the Middle West, 1900-1939* (Madison: University of Wisconsin Press, 1951), pp. 453-54. For the two most famous statements of the early plans, see W. J. Spillman, *Balancing the Farm Output* (New York: Orange Judd Publishing Co., 1927), and John D. Black, *Agricultural Reform in the United States* (New York: McGraw-Hill Book Co., 1929), Chap. 10.

[20] Joseph S. Davis, *On Agricultural Policy, 1926-1938* (Palo Alto, California: Stanford University Food Research Institute, 1939), p. 208; and Russell Lord, *The Wallaces of Iowa* (Boston: Houghton Mifflin Co., 1947), Chap. 9.

[21] Saloutos and Hicks, *op. cit.*, p. 454.

[22] A brief sketch of Wilson's role is given in Richard S. Kirkendall, "Four

[23] At least so he appeared to the present author in personal interviews in Economists in the Political Process," *Journal of Farm Economics*, XLI (May, 1959), 194-210. August, 1959. He may not have been so detached earlier.

[24] Wilson, personal interview, August 18, 1959.

[25] *Ibid.*

sponsible farm groups themselves agree on."[26] More specific recognition of Farm Bureau leaders was evinced when Roosevelt conferred with some of them in Chicago. Clifford Gregory says that he, Ed O'Neal, and Earl Smith conferred with Roosevelt in the autumn of 1932 in the Congress Hotel in Chicago, and that Roosevelt told them, in effect: "One of the first things I am going to do is to take steps to restore farm prices. I am going to call farmers' leaders together, lock them in a room, and tell them not to come out until they have agreed on a plan."[27] A biographer of George Peek states that early in October, 1932, Roosevelt and Henry Morgenthau met with Peek, Chester Davis, Earl Smith, Ed O'Neal, and Clifford Gregory in Chicago.[28] Whether or not this was the same conference is not clear, but the point is that Roosevelt did confer with O'Neal and Earl Smith, among others. Farm organization leaders were much impressed by this sort of recognition of their efforts, and those Midwestern farm leaders who were traditionally Republican did not forget it in the campaign of 1936. As for George Peek, his reaction was: "It looks to me as though in the campaign for Roosevelt . . . we are in the last trenches and if he is not elected that agriculture is doomed to peasantry."[29]

Clifford Gregory says that Roosevelt's main campaign speech on farm policy, the Topeka speech, September 14, 1932, was generally understood in informed farm circles to be indicating his support for the sort of domestic allotment plan which M. L. Wilson had been vigorously sponsoring for years.[30] That this was correct is proved by evidence that Wilson, who had been taken to Roosevelt by Rexford G. Tugwell, had written a rough draft which Roosevelt drew upon for that speech.[31] While not all the farm organization leaders favored the particular scheme embodied in the voluntary domestic allotment plan, they acclaimed Roosevelt's unmistakable intention to do something for the farmer.

---

[26] Gregory, *op. cit.*, p. 152.

[27] *Ibid.*

[28] Gilbert C. Fite, *George N. Peek and the Fight for Farm Parity* (Norman: University of Oklahoma Press, 1954), p. 239. Fite's statement is based on a letter from Peek in the Peek Papers, located in the University of Missouri Library.

[29] Peek to Earl Smith, October 18, 1932, quoted *ibid.*

[30] Gregory, *op. cit.*, p. 152.

[31] Fite, *op. cit.*, p. 239. Fite bases his statement in part on the rough draft of Wilson's suggestions which is in the Roosevelt Papers at Hyde Park. Partial confirmation is found in Tugwell's statement that the Topeka speech was written by Wilson and Mordecai Ezekiel, while Tugwell himself made it sound like Roosevelt. Tugwell, personal interview, November 29, 1949.

The farm organizations did attempt to get together on their efforts in 1932 and early 1933, before the inauguration of Roosevelt. In the A.F.B.F. files are the minutes of several joint conferences between the Farm Bureau, the Grange, the Farmers' Union, and the major co-operatives, which were held in an attempt to co-ordinate their efforts. According to the minutes, one such conference was called by O'Neal and met on October 11 and 12, 1932, in Chicago. Present besides farm organization leaders were several outstanding representatives of the agricultural press, including Henry A. Wallace and Clifford Gregory.[32] Clifford Gregory tells of another such meeting on October 28.[33] The minutes of still another meeting, held in Washington on December 12, 13, and 14, 1932, indicate that O'Neal acted as chairman of the group, and virtually the same farm organizations were listed as previously, with the addition of a counsel, Frederic P. Lee, and three "economic advisers," Mordecai Ezekiel of the Federal Farm Board, William Myers of Cornell University, and Rexford Tugwell of Columbia University, as well as Henry Morgenthau. Henry A. Wallace is not listed as being present at this meeting.[34] Since the minutes of these meetings were written by M. S. Winder, Secretary of the A.F.B.F., who acted as secretary of the conferences, it may be that they overemphasized the role of the A.F.B.F. leaders in these preinaugural meetings. However, since they were not for publication, there was no special reason why they should do so. It would certainly appear from these minutes that O'Neal took a leading part in trying to get agreement among the farm organizations, in accordance with the expressed wish of Roosevelt. It was in preinaugural conferences such as these, says Earl Smith, that the basic principles of the New Deal farm program were agreed upon, rather than in the more publicized meeting of agricultural leaders on March 10, 1933, which was called by Henry A. Wallace.[35]

The conference called by Wallace to meet just six days after the inauguration was of basic significance, however, so far as the relationship between the government and the farm organizations was concerned. It seemed to be an official recognition of the right of

[32] "Minutes of the Conference of Agricultural Leaders . . . Chicago, Illinois, October 11-12, 1932," A.F.B.F., O'Neal Papers. Gregory, *op. cit.*, mentions the same meeting.

[33] *Ibid.*, p. 155.

[34] "Minutes of the Conference of Agricultural Leaders . . . Washington, D.C., December 12-14, 1932," A.F.B.F., O'Neal Papers; Gregory, *op. cit.*

[35] Smith, personal interview, July 18, 1949.

farm organization leaders to be consulted in the making of national agricultural policy. This meeting set the precedent for the practice of consultation which may have been looked upon by the Roosevelt administration as a grant of privilege only, but which became in Farm Bureau thinking an inalienable right.

On March 8, 1933, O'Neal jubilantly announced to the board of directors of the A.F.B.F. that he had received a telephone call from the Secretary of Agriculture, Henry A. Wallace. According to O'Neal, the Secretary requested representatives of the A.F.B.F. to attend a meeting of agricultural leaders to be held at the Department of Agriculture on March 10 to consider agricultural legislation. There is no hint of undue excitement, however, in the dry statement found in the minutes that the board approved the request.[36]

In addition, the board decided that O'Neal should send a telegram to Roosevelt urging him to recommend the following measures in his message to the forthcoming special session of Congress: (1) government guarantee of the new deposits of all banks, and protection of the interests of rural banking equal to that given to city banking; (2) approval of the recommendations of Professor George Warren regarding monetary reform; (3) the restoration of price parity for agricultural commodities with the products of industry; and (4) relief of distressed mortgage indebtedness.[37] Later at the same meeting a motion was passed urging the adoption of the allotment plan together with a tariff on imported fats and oils.

Thus it is quite clear that before Roosevelt presented his farm bill, and even before the meeting of the group called by Wallace, the A.F.B.F. had already endorsed the main principles which were to be embodied in the Agricultural Adjustment Act of 1933.[38] An

---

[36] A.F.B.F., *Minutes of the Board of Directors*, March 8-9, 1933.

[37] *Ibid.*

[38] The aim of the Agricultural Adjustment Act of 1933 was to raise the price of farm commodities to the parity level, by controlling (or "adjusting") production of the so-called basic crops. The Agricultural Adjustment Administration (usually known as the A.A.A.) was set up to administer the act. George Peek was the first administrator, and he was succeeded by Chester Davis. Under the A.A.A., individual producers of the so-called basic crops—corn, cotton, wheat, rice, tobacco, and peanuts—were assigned an acreage allotment, which was ordinarily a percentage of the acreage which that farmer had planted during the previous five years. In return for carrying out contracts with the government to reduce their crops to the allotted acreage, farmers received benefit payments. These were financed chiefly by means of processing taxes levied upon the first domestic processing of the farm commodity concerned. Production control committees, on which local farmers served, assisted in the determination of individual acreage allotments and in checking compliance with the contracts.

exception to this was the rider concerning tariffs on fats and oils which Earl Smith of Illinois proposed and which the board adopted.[39] But the principles underlying the three main agencies through which President Roosevelt's early farm program operated —the Farm Credit Administration, the monetary program, and the Agricultural Adjustment Administration—were all urged upon the President before he submitted his recommendations to Congress.

Further discussion of the monetary question at the A.F.B.F. board meeting resulted in the passage of a motion that in the event that adoption of the Warren plan could not be secured, the free coinage of silver at the ratio of 16 to 1 should be supported.[40] While the Warren plan was always dearest to the hearts of the New York and New England delegations, Earl Smith of Illinois spoke favorably of the prominent place that might be given to silver.[41] The Populist tradition on the monetary question and the agrarian spirit of the Bryan campaign of 1896 thus found echoes in the Farm Bureau policies of 1933.

A more startling manifestation of harmony with the views of the Roosevelt administration was given in the discussion of Muscle Shoals. President Roosevelt's recommendations regarding Muscle Shoals were presented, and the Farm Bureau resolved to support Roosevelt's policy, "provided the production of sufficient quantities of cheap fertilizer is included in the plan proposed."[42] This was an endorsement by the A.F.B.F. of the proposal for the establishment of the Tennessee Valley Authority in advance of Roosevelt's presentation of it to Congress. The first part of this A.F.B.F. resolution in essence pledged Farm Bureau support for government operation of Muscle Shoals. This was a dramatic reversal of previous Farm Bureau policy, which in recent years had favored operation of Muscle Shoals by Henry Ford. The second part—the emphasis on the use of the power to be produced there to provide cheap fertilizer—was a repetition of the Farm Bureau's traditional demand.

The one major policy closely affecting agriculture on which the Farm Bureau differed with Roosevelt in the period immediately following his inauguration was that of the reciprocal trade policy. At the same meeting of the board of directors, on March 8, 1933, in which policies virtually identical with Roosevelt's own were endorsed, a lengthy discussion of tariffs and reciprocal trade agree-

---

[39] A.F.B.F., *Minutes of the Board of Directors*, March 8-9, 1933.
[40] *Ibid.*
[41] *Ibid.*
[42] *Ibid.*

ments revealed that several board members feared that the interests of agriculture might be sacrificed in the negotiation of reciprocal trade agreements. Accordingly, a motion proposed by two Midwesterners (one of them was Earl Smith) was carried: "That we oppose any reciprocal trade agreements that do not adequately safeguard the interests of agriculture."[43] It took several more years of skillful mediation before O'Neal could bring the Midwestern and Southern sections of the Farm Bureau together on this point, and in harmony with the Roosevelt administration.

According to Henry A. Wallace, the reason why he (and Tugwell) called the farm leaders to meet in Washington on March 10 was "to see if they could agree on farm legislation."[44] Wallace says that the conference almost split on commodity differences,[45] while Clifford Gregory gives a somewhat different impression in his statement that it was the most harmonious farm meeting he had ever attended.[46] Apparently harmony was attained by agreement upon the idea that a broad grant of authority should be made to the U.S. Department of Agriculture so that flexibility in the choice of means to suit the various commodities would be possible. It was also agreed that the goal of the new legislation should be "parity"[47]—the idea of the fair-exchange value for which George Peek and the McNary-Haugenites had long been pushing.

The Farm Bureau had before now identified itself with the goal of "parity," and most of the other farm organizations were willing to go along with this objective too. But there was one which was not, and that was the Farmers' Union, which still called for "cost of production." The president of the Farmers' Union at that period was John Simpson, who had not been present at some of the preinaugural "unity" conferences nor at the postinaugural conference of March 10.[48] Congressman Lambertson represented the Farmers' Union at the latter conference,[49] as well as at some of the former ones.

Later the Farmers' Union withdrew its endorsement of the principles agreed upon by the farm leaders in the postinaugural conference, and tried to get a cost-of-production amendment to the

---

[43] *Ibid.*

[44] Wallace, *op. cit.,* pp. 162-63.

[45] *Ibid.*

[46] Gregory, *op. cit.,* p. 156; Schlesinger, *op. cit.,* p. 38. Schlesinger describes the meeting as taking place on March 16.

[47] Wallace, *op. cit.,* pp. 162-63; Gregory, *op. cit.,* p. 156.

[48] Wallace, *op. cit.,* p. 167.

[49] Gregory, *op. cit.,* p. 156.

Agricultural Adjustment bill when it was before Congress, but failed.[50] Wallace himself recommended that it be struck out.[51] Unity on the farm organization front, therefore, was not quite complete in 1933. John Simpson was considered something of a maverick, and he was never close to the Roosevelt administration.

Speaking of the report of the farm leaders to the President, agreed upon in the conference of March 10-11, 1933, Chester Davis told the Farm Bureau later (after he had become administrator of the A.A.A.): "The Farm Bureau Federation and its state representatives had more to do with fixing the line of that report to the President, which he adopted literally in his message to Congress, than any other force represented there."[52]

Against this background it is not surprising that the A.F.B.F. was prone to claim credit for the early New Deal farm program. Over and over in the years to follow, Farm Bureau leaders reiterated the theme: It was our program, and the President had the good sense to adopt it.

While this belief is understandable and seems to have been honestly held, it requires considerable modification as a statement of fact.

The A.F.B.F. was not responsible for the creative ideas on which the New Deal farm program was based. As one Administration spokesman succinctly put it: "The Farm Bureau never creates anything. It supports." The creative minds with whom the ideas for the New Deal farm program originated were a sort of "agricultural brain trust"[53] of philosophical thinkers, economists, university professors, and publicists, who had been thinking about these matters for many years. Prominent among them were M. L. Wilson, W. J. Spillman, John D. Black, Mordecai Ezekiel, George Warren, George Peek, Rexford Tugwell, and Henry A. Wallace himself. W. J. Spillman has been credited by one writer as being "the basic inventor" of the A.A.A.[54] Beardsley Ruml was also one of the pioneers, considered by some to be equal in importance to Spillman.

Nor did President Roosevelt simply take over, lock, stock, and barrel, a program sponsored by the Farm Bureau. It is true that

[50] *Ibid.*
[51] Wallace, *op. cit.*, p. 167.
[52] *A.F.B.F. Official News Letter,* October 30, 1934. The quotation is from a speech made by Chester Davis to the Western Farm Bureau regional meeting.
[53] The phrase was used by Paul H. Appleby, personal interview, August 18, 1959.
[54] Russell Lord, *The Agrarian Revival* (New York: American Association for Adult Education, 1939), p. 145.

"parity" was the heart of the A.A.A. as it had been of the McNary-Haugen thinking, which the A.F.B.F. had long supported, but there were many forces besides the A.F.B.F. which independently urged upon Roosevelt a program to achieve this goal. As to the means, in order to get agreement among the farm forces, practically everyone's scheme was included in the Agricultural Adjustment Act, and it was left largely to the Administration to choose from among them.

The fact that Frederic P. Lee, who had an important part in drafting the Agricultural Adjustment bill,[55] was then employed by the A.F.B.F. has little significance. The Farm Bureau was no doubt glad to have him there, but his part was that of a first-rate technician whom all respected (he had been for many years legislative counsel for the Senate), rather than that of a representative of the Farm Bureau.

The A.F.B.F.'s role in the making of the New Deal for agriculture was nevertheless a crucial one, for two reasons. First, it served as a unifying agency within agriculture, both in bringing about sectional agreement between the Southern and the Midwestern farmers within its own organization, and (under the leadership of President O'Neal) in working earnestly in 1932 to bring about agreement among the major farm organizations. Second, as Henry A. Wallace himself has stated, the Farm Bureau gave the Department of Agriculture its strongest political support.[56] Wallace did not elaborate this statement, but a study of the activities and statements of Farm Bureau leaders indicates that such support consisted both in winning farmer support at the local level and in pressing Congress on the national level. By virtue of its federal structure, the Farm Bureau was superbly equipped to do both.

The history of both the A.F.B.F. and of the New Deal would have been different if any other man than Ed O'Neal had been president of the A.F.B.F. during that critical period.[57] The role of personalities was a significant one particularly in the early New Deal period.

The best assessment of O'Neal is that of M. L. Wilson. "O'Neal was a mediator," says Wilson. "He brought together the South and the Midwest. And Wallace thought so too."[58]

---

[55] Wallace, *op. cit.*, pp. 164-65, is among those who credit Lee with this part, but like most others fails to mention the fact that Lee was then employed by the A.F.B.F.

[56] Wallace, personal interview, August 27, 1959.

[57] O'Neal was president of the A.F.B.F. from 1931 to 1947.

[58] Wilson, personal interview, August 18, 1959.

Wallace spoke for himself in 1934, when he wrote in *New Fron-tiers* of the personalities involved in the campaign for farm relief, from 1922 to that date: "I think of Ed O'Neal who worked so un-ceasingly to heal the ancient breach between the Democratic farm-ers of the South and the Republican farmers of the Middle West."[59]

In addition to being a mediator, O'Neal was a Democrat. He was a friend of education. And he was a hard-drinking Presbyterian. O'Neal did not mind saying he was a Democrat. He always had been. Besides, he liked President Roosevelt. He liked Henry Wal-lace. And he even liked Rex Tugwell, though sometimes he dis-agreed with his ideas. He understood these people. On the other hand, Earl Smith saw red when Rex Tugwell's name was men-tioned.

O'Neal was a Southern aristrocrat of the old school—the type whom William Faulkner describes as being progressively displaced in the South by the Snopes family. Owner of a plantation which he had inherited in the Tennessee Valley region of northern Ala-bama,[60] O'Neal was no dirt farmer, but he had the affection for farming and the interest in intelligent methods of agriculture of an eighteenth-century English gentleman. It was while he was on a tour of Europe (he made the "grand tour" of a young Southern gentleman after his graduation from Washington and Lee College) that he said he got the idea of better farming. When he came back home, he went to the land-grant colleges at Auburn, Alabama, and at Urbana, Illinois, where he acquired some solid basis for his in-spiration for intelligent methods. He became a staunch supporter of agricultural education as carried out by the Alabama Extension Service, and an early supporter of the Farm Bureau work sponsored by the Extension Service in Alabama. He attempted to make a model of his own farm to show that under progressive methods of cultivation "that old red land"[61] of the former cotton kingdom could be made as productive and rich as any in the world.

O'Neal had no desire to change the social order of his region. But he had a paternalistic interest in improving conditions for all, both high and low. It was M. L. Wilson's impression that O'Neal

---

[59] Wallace, *op. cit.*, p. 159.

[60] O'Neal, personal interview, May 23-24, 1949. Biographical details are also based on *Who's Who in America*, XXIV (1946-47), 1783; a press release by the A.F.B.F. department of information about 1931, A.F.B.F., O'Neal Papers; "The Farm Bureau," *Fortune*, June, 1944, p. 156; *Current Biography*, 1946, pp. 436-38; and P. O. Davis, *One Man: Edward Asbury O'Neal III of Alabama* (Auburn: Alabama Polytechnic Institute, 1945).

[61] One of O'Neal's favorite expressions.

was something like Senator Bankhead, who, going around little farms in Alabama and talking with even the lowest Negro farmers, said: "We must do something to give opportunities to these people."[62] Bankhead may have been more willing to alter the system. O'Neal wished to give them greater opportunities within the existing social order. In this matter O'Neal was representative of his section, for welfare policies generally had far greater support within the A.F.B.F. from the Southern section than from the Midwestern, where Farm Bureau members simply saw no need for them.

At first Midwestern farmers, as staunchly Protestant as they were Republican, were bewildered by the fact that O'Neal openly both cursed and drank, in the manner of a gentleman, but not according to their conception of a Presbyterian. Their initial wariness soon dissolved. According to the testimony of Midwestern leaders who knew him well, the Midwestern farmers came to love him and to forgive in him the "vices" which they would not have tolerated in anyone else.

Besides agricultural reform, O'Neal's other great enthusiasm was for his own region—that of northern Alabama and Nashville, Tennessee, the heart of the Tennessee Valley. His attitude toward it was more that of a Westerner of 1812 than of a Southerner. It was Andrew Jackson's old region, and O'Neal's great-grandfather, Alex Coffee, had been a close friend and partner of Jackson in land speculation. O'Neal treasured family correspondence between his ancestors and Jackson.[63]

In Franklin D. Roosevelt, O'Neal felt that he had found a kindred spirit who shared his enthusiasm for Andrew Jackson and for Jacksonian principles. Letters from Roosevelt to O'Neal reveal that at one time or another O'Neal sent him a picture pertaining to the Coffee family's connection with Andrew Jackson,[64] a newspaper clipping about Jackson,[65] and some of Jackson's correspondence which was in O'Neal's possession. Roosevelt always seems to have expressed his appreciation, a typical Roosevelt reply being: "Those letters from good old Andrew Jackson are magnificent. It is absolutely true that his opponents represented the same social outlook and the same element in the population that ours do."[66]

[62] Wilson, personal interview, August 18, 1959.
[63] O'Neal showed some of this correspondence to the author. It seems from comments made by various people that he showed these letters to everybody.
[64] Roosevelt to O'Neal, November 26, 1940 (photostat).
[65] Roosevelt to O'Neal, February 1, 1943 (photostat).
[66] Roosevelt to O'Neal, December 1, 1933, in O'Neal personal collection, Florence, Alabama.

It was when agricultural prices slid so low that not even "brains on the land"[67] or Muscle Shoals could save the farmers that O'Neal realized that "I had to step aside and stabilize American agriculture. Earl Smith helped me to stabilize agriculture."[68] O'Neal was never backward, as his colleagues could testify, about taking personal credit for great accomplishments, while generously acknowledging the assistance of others. Earl Smith, always loyal, was nevertheless sometimes irked by O'Neal's expectation of such assistance, particularly when it involved pulling the chestnuts out of the fire created by O'Neal's impulsiveness.[69]

There have been many, however, who looked upon Earl Smith rather than Ed O'Neal as the real power in the A.F.B.F., and as the brains behind the Farm Bureau throne.[70] This is no more correct than O'Neal's estimate of the situation. Actually the two complemented each other. O'Neal was the harmonizer; Smith, the man of action. Each in fact typified his section. The strength of the South lay in its agricultural population, which gave it political power. The strength of Midwestern agriculture lay in its wealth, which gave it economic as well as political power. Each in its own way was therefore the leading agricultural section, and the alliance of the two through the Farm Bureau and through the harmonious relations of their leaders gave the A.F.B.F. power which no other farm organization in the United States could hope to match, unless perchance another organization could find a strong ally outside agriculture.

Earl Smith liked the role of the able businessman who had built up the outstandingly successful commercial services of the Illinois Agricultural Association. That O'Neal could not even manage his own business and was not particularly interested in doing so was common knowledge, but this did not reduce his stature as a political genius. Earl Smith was an able and experienced politician as well, for he had long been immersed in the politics of McNary-Haugenism. In acknowledging the Farm Bureau as a splendid source of political support for the Department of Agriculture in the early New Deal farm program, Henry A. Wallace characterized Earl Smith as the best fighter of all, exceptionally capable, and

---

[67] Another of O'Neal's favorite expressions.
[68] O'Neal, personal interview, May 23-24, 1949.
[69] This was said by old-timers on the A.F.B.F. staff.
[70] Earl Smith was for many years president of the Illinois Agricultural Association and a member of the board of directors of the A.F.B.F. He became vice-president of the A.F.B.F. in 1936.

dominating.[71] Frank O. Lowden called Earl Smith "the ablest of all farm leaders."[72]

Though O'Neal was a Democrat and Earl Smith was a Republican, both believed in "keeping the farm program out of politics." On the face of it, this was an absurd statement since both were so deeply involved in politics. They simply meant that the farm program should be bipartisan, as the old Farm Bloc had been, and this was a sacred precept especially with Earl Smith.

Smith was the symbol of corn, the great crop of the Midwest, while O'Neal symbolized the cotton South. (Some of the independent commodity organizations maintained that cotton had no real spokesman in the Farm Bureau, and in fact O'Neal sometimes had more difficulty in keeping unity among cotton farmers than in keeping unity between corn and cotton.) One of Smith's great sources of strength was his rational approach to farm problems, compared to the emotional appeal which agrarian reformers were prone to make. Typical of his approach was the sort of statement which he made many times at meetings of the board of directors, in words to this effect: "If you boys can decide what you want for cotton, and it is not in conflict with the basic philosophy of the A.F.B.F., we will help you get it. And we expect you to do the same for us for corn. Let's forget about oils and what it may do to them, and stick to the basic things." A man of this nature was not the sort who leads crusades, but he was amenable to compromise, so long as it was rational. Ed O'Neal could exhort A.F.B.F. leaders "to go out and preach the gospel,"[73] but Earl Smith was more plain-spoken.

A third significant figure, who was somewhat separate from both the Roosevelt administration and the Farm Bureau although he had close connections with both, was Clifford Gregory, editor of the *Prairie Farmer.* Gregory was another mediator. He had been a college classmate and close friend of Henry A. Wallace. *He* could influence Earl Smith—though few people could. Also he could influence Ed O'Neal somewhat. He therefore acted as a mediator at times between the Farm Bureau and the Department of Agriculture.[74]

Farm Bureau leaders believed not only that it was their program which the Roosevelt administration had adopted in the Agricultural

[71] Wallace, personal interview, August 27, 1959.
[72] Hutchinson, *op. cit.,* p. 279.
[73] A.F.B.F., *Minutes of the Board of Directors,* June 5-6, 1935.
[74] This interpretation of the place of Clifford Gregory is based on statements by M. L. Wilson, personal interview, August 29, 1959.

Adjustment Act, but that the Farm Bureau was responsible for the choice of Henry A. Wallace as Secretary of Agriculture. A rumor had gone around Farm Bureau circles that Roosevelt was contemplating the appointment of Henry Morgenthau to this position, whereupon Farm Bureau leaders recommended Henry Wallace.[75] O'Neal's account of the matter is approximately as follows:

> I had got to know Roosevelt while he was Governor of New York, through the people in the land-grant college at Cornell. In 1929 I brought him to the farmers at our national Farm Bureau convention. At a state fair in Syracuse, New York, I rode with him, and he said: "I am planning to run for President. Will you advise me?" I said: "I should be delighted." Later, at the preinaugural conferences, a man from the wheat co-ops got up and read a telegram from his members endorsing Morgenthau for Secretary of Agriculture. I knew this would never do. I caught Rex Tugwell's eye, motioned him out, and said, "This will never do." Then I called Roosevelt's secretary and said I had to see Roosevelt next day. I went out to Hyde Park to his study, and told him: "You ought not to do this. Morgenthau would be fine for Secretary of the Treasury, or something like that. But these fellows from the South and Midwest elected you." The Midwest had gone Democratic. Then I suggested Henry Wallace. I didn't know him personally, but I knew his father, and he was mighty fine. F.D.R. held out his hand and said: "I will do it."[76]

Of course, added O'Neal, Wallace was a Midwesterner, and so were Chester Davis and George Peek, but the President was not going to appoint a Southerner. He did not have to—he knew he had the South.

Rex Tugwell, who was in a good position to know, says that Roosevelt may have let the Farm Bureau leaders think that it was at their suggestion that he appointed Henry Wallace, but that actually he never had any intention of appointing Henry Morgenthau as Secretary of Agriculture, and that he had already decided on Wallace at an earlier date.[77] Furthermore, there seems to have been a whole crop of stories as to why and how Roosevelt came to appoint Wallace.[78]

The Farm Bureau story is relevant not as a statement of fact but as a statement of belief. The leaders of the A.F.B.F., both Democratic and Republican, endorsed Wallace and welcomed him. They thought they had chosen him.

---

[75] The author was told the story independently by a number of Farm Bureau leaders.

[76] O'Neal, personal interview, May 23-24, 1949.

[77] Tugwell, personal interview, November 29, 1949.

[78] One of these was that it was a tossup between Henry Wallace and Clifford Gregory, and that Morgenthau had whispered in Roosevelt's ear in favor of Wallace. This was the rumor around the *Prairie Farmer* office.

By the time of the quarterly meeting of the board of directors of the A.F.B.F. on August 16 and 17, 1933, the Agricultural Adjustment Act and some emergency acts of the New Deal already had a trial period. There seem to have been three chief reactions of the A.F.B.F. leaders at this time. The first was that the farm organizations, especially the A.F.B.F., were responsible for the enactment of the legislation, and therefore must accept the responsibility of working for its success. Among the declarations of this sort was one by President O'Neal: "The farmer-producer, through his organizations, the Farm Bureau and co-operatives, has laid down the rules for the New Deal for agriculture. It is going to be just too bad if we now do not achieve success. If we fail to do something constructive for the farmers at this time, then someone else will take the leadership and do the things that need to be done. We have got to take the responsibility for this legislation because we certainly are responsible for it. Leaders of the administration know this."[79]

The second reaction was that the A.F.B.F. must be given credit for this legislation and must take advantage of this favorable situation for building membership. There were some complaints that "the administration was taking all the credit it could get and giving no proper recognition to the farm organizations. . . ."[80] Ed O'Neal and Earl Smith were more inclined to emphasize that President Roosevelt had publicly stated that he had taken the program of the farm organizations in fulfillment of his pledge that if they could agree on a program he would take it and put it through. There was no dissent to the statement: "We must take advantage of our legislative accomplishments to go out and build up a big membership . . . we must impress our people with the fact that payment of dues is necessary if the organization is to carry on, and that, had it not been for the organization, the results achieved in the last Congress would not have been forthcoming."[81]

The third reaction was that the securing of favorable legislation by the Farm Bureau was not enough; it was necessary also for the Farm Bureau to influence the administration of the laws. O'Neal declared: "If we are not invited to consult with administrative leaders, then we must go in and present to them our point of view regardless. If we make enough fuss and are persistent enough, they

---

[79] A.F.B.F., *Minutes of the Board of Directors,* August 16-17, 1933.
[80] *Ibid.*
[81] *Ibid.*

will give heed to our wishes and our advice. If we will build up our membership no one will want to disregard our advice on matters of policy or administration."[82] One director expressed the belief that the problem was not so much to establish a good relationship with the central administration, for "officials at Washington seem to want to contact with us and enjoy our advice," but rather "how to break into the administration in our various states."[83] Earl Smith, however, felt that he had been able to assure "proper representation" of the Illinois Agricultural Association in the various conferences called by the officials of the A.A.A., and he told of the methods used.[84]

At this same meeting, the board of directors passed a resolution, a copy of which was voted to be sent to Secretary Wallace and to George Peek, Administrator of the A.A.A., commending them for calling in the Extension Service of the land-grant colleges and the teachers of vocational agriculture and for using them in the administration of the act.[85] Nothing could have suited the Farm Bureau better than to have the Agricultural Adjustment Act administered on the local level through the county agents, but the Farm Bureau was not responsible for the decision to use them. To Department of Agriculture officials it seemed at that time the logical and desirable thing to do, especially as time was pressing.[86]

At the end of 1933, the leaders again reported on relationships with the Administration. "I don't think," said Earl Smith, "President Roosevelt is going clear through if the other crowd succeeds in getting control of sufficient public sentiment—then he will wilt. . . . Increase our membership; then we will save agriculture, also the nation."[87] President O'Neal was more sanguine of the influence of the A.F.B.F. over the Administration. He explained that "the administration is sympathetic toward us and that they ask our advice and help; that the administration gets in trouble and goes contrary to our advice sometimes, but that they always come back."[88] *Fortune* magazine says of O'Neal: "In the early New Deal he counted himself the President's private tutor on farm affairs—and considered

---

[82] *Ibid.*
[83] *Ibid.*
[84] *Ibid.*
[85] *Ibid.*
[86] Paul H. Appleby, personal interview, August 18, 1959. See also Lord, *The Agrarian Revival*, pp. 161-62. Lord thinks it was M. L. Wilson who was most influential in the decision to use the Extension Service.
[87] A.F.B.F., *Minutes of the Board of Directors*, December 7-8, 1933.
[88] *Ibid.*

the President a promising student."[89] The statement seems to be perfectly correct.

The reactions to the A.A.A. in the four regions which composed the A.F.B.F. varied, of course, as did the benefits which each derived or expected to derive. The South was for it, the Northeast against it, the West divided or indifferent. The Midwest was the uncertain region, where attitudes were most likely to shift, and it is therefore deserving of special attention.

It was quite well recognized within the A.F.B.F. that the A.A.A. was a program chiefly for Southern and Midwestern agriculture. In 1935, for example, it was assumed that the membership campaign based on taking credit for the A.A.A. would be carried on mainly in the Midwest and the South, "because of the fact that most of the contract signers are located in these regions."[90] An analysis of the votes in Congress on the Agricultural Adjustment Act of 1933, made by A.F.B.F. officials, was interpreted by them as evidence that the legislation was passed as a result of a nonpartisan Midwestern-Southern alliance. This analysis, including check marks which were on the original, is given in Table 3. That the vote could have been interpreted also as a Democratic Party victory is indicated by the number of Republican votes for and against, but this was not the sort of thing that was discussed officially in A.F.B.F. circles, where the creed of nonpartisanship was supreme.

At first, Midwestern Farm Bureau leaders had every right to feel pleased about the degree to which the Farm Bureau was consulted by the Administration. Earl Smith always maintained that Roosevelt had adopted, in the A.A.A., the program of the farm organizations (especially the A.F.B.F.). Furthermore, it was still fresh in his memory, years later, that Roosevelt had been willing to accept, as Hoover had not, the proposal for an emergency loan on corn made by Earl Smith himself.[91] This corn loan, of 45 cents a bushel (at a time when the country price of corn in Illinois was 23 cents), which was rushed into effect before the more slow-moving A.A.A. program of production control could get under way, did

---

[89] "The Farm Bureau," *Fortune,* June, 1944, p. 156. This article is usually attributed to J. K. Galbraith, who was formerly on the staff of the A.F.B.F. as its economist.

[90] A.F.B.F., *Minutes of the Board of Directors,* June 5-6, 1935.

[91] Smith told this story to the annual convention of the Illinois Agricultural Association, Chicago, Illinois, November 15-18, 1948, which the writer attended. The story is also told in the *Illinois Agricultural Association Record* in various places, though Smith's personal role is omitted.

TABLE 3

*Congressional Voting Record on the 1933
Agricultural Adjustment Act* [a]

Section	Original House Bill		Final Senate Bill	
	Votes For	Votes Against	Votes For	Votes Against
East	65	62	6	11
South	109 √	4	20 √	2
Midwest	106 √	26	15 √	7
West	35	6	12	8
Total Votes	315	98	53	28
Republican Votes	38	72	13	17

[a] Source: A.F.B.F., O'Neal Papers, "Sectional Vote Records, 1928-1942."

more than anything else, Smith believed, to give hope to the Midwestern farmers in 1933, and to prevent them from resorting to such remedies as those proposed by the Farmers' Holiday Association.[92] Moreover, the executive committee of the national Corn-Hog Committee, which is most famous for its recommendation of "the killing of the little pigs" as an emergency price-raising measure, was composed of five members, three of whom were prominently associated with the A.F.B.F.[93] Earl Smith was chairman of this executive committee, and Ed O'Neal (certainly no corn-hog farmer) and Clifford Gregory were on it. Among the other members of the full committee of 25 were three other members of the A.F.B.F. board of directors—Settle of Indiana, Brown of Missouri, and Olson of Minnesota—as well as other state farm bureau leaders.[94]

Further evidence of the favorable attitude of the Midwestern Farm Bureau leaders toward the A.A.A. was revealed in a discussion at the Midwest Farm Bureau presidents' and secretaries' conference in March, 1934, in which each state reported on the progress of the A.A.A. There was general agreement that the corn-hog program was

---

[92] *Ibid.*

[93] "Report of the National Corn-Hog Committee of Twenty-five at Informal Conference, Washington, D.C., August 10, 1933," A.F.B.F., O'Neal Papers; "Minutes of the Meeting of the Corn-Hog Producers' Committee with Representatives of the A.A.A. and the U.S.D.A., U.S.D.A. Offices, August 7, 1933," *ibid.*; "Minutes of the Meeting with the Packers' Committee, U.S.D.A. Offices, August 9, 1933," *ibid.* To deal with the very low price of hogs, in September, 1933, the government bought and slaughtered 6,000,000 little pigs, to reduce the hog population and thus prevent the price from falling still further.

[94] A.F.B.F., "Administrative Report," *Minutes of the Board of Directors,* August 16-17, 1933.

going well and had widespread support, that the dairy program was most unsatisfactory, and there was disagreement as to how the wheat program was going.[95] Earl Smith stated that the Farm Bureau had "practically run" the A.A.A. program in Illinois, to the extent that when the permanent A.A.A. committee was set up, the Farm Bureau had to ask that one member be a non–Farm Bureau member.[96] The Indiana representative declared: "A.A.A. program has been Farm Bureau in Indiana."[97] There were also some critical comments, of which a typical one was that there were "too many professors there in Washington writing bulletins and more bulletins and telling the folks in the county what to do."[98] The general tenor of the discussion was, however, that the Midwestern Farm Bureau leaders were favorable to the A.A.A. and felt a responsibility for helping to make it a success.

---

[95] "Proceedings of the Midwest Presidents, Secretaries, and Organization Directors . . . Chicago, Illinois, March 26-27, 1934," A.F.B.F. regional files, folder marked "R. W. Blackburn."

[96] *Ibid.*

[97] *Ibid.*

[98] *Ibid.*

CHAPTER V

Sectional Conflict: The Threatened
Revolt of the Northeast

In 1934 and for a number of years afterward, the Northeastern region of the Farm Bureau was in a state of near revolt, or secession from the A.F.B.F., in protest against the endorsement of the A.A.A. There is little doubt that during the first years of the New Deal the major policy of the A.F.B.F. was embodied in the A.A.A., which the A.F.B.F. not only endorsed but claimed the credit for inaugurating. While this policy was of vital assistance in membership building in the Southern region, it was a serious handicap that had to be overcome by higher strategy in the Northeast, where many farmers felt not only that the A.A.A. was doing them no good, but that it was actually harming them. The story is significant in that it provides insight into (1) sectional conflict within American agriculture; (2) how the A.F.B.F. functioned in bridging over these conflicts; and (3) the decentralized structure of the A.F.B.F.

The conflict was stirred up, as all agreed, by the farm press, specifically in articles by Howard E. Babcock in the *American Agriculturist*. This was an outstanding New York state farm paper, which was taken over in 1934 by a group of four men (including Babcock) when Henry Morgenthau, former editor-owner, went to Washington. The A.F.B.F. board of directors was much disturbed by the Babcock articles.[1] Babcock himself agreed that he was "needling the boys," adding that they needed it.[2] Clifford Gregory took up the counterattack for the Midwest in the *Prairie Farmer*, which was probably the most influential farm paper in the Midwest, with the possible exception of *Wallace's Farmer*.

---

[1] A.F.B.F., "Minutes of the Executive Committee," *Minutes of the Board of Directors*, June 20-22, 1934.
[2] Babcock, personal interview, March 21, 1949.

As president of the A.F.B.F., O'Neal, to whom unity within agriculture was of paramount importance, was fearful of an open break, yet he was neither willing to give up the policy of endorsement of the A.A.A. nor able directly to interfere in Northeastern Farm Bureau affairs. The revolt that threatened was a rank and file matter, for most of the Northeastern Farm Bureau leaders were convinced, as was O'Neal, that if farmers in any one section were to get what they wanted, they must seek compromise within a national organization with a national program.

Babcock's chief accusation against the A.F.B.F. was that the national organization was being used chiefly to promote a sectional policy—that is, the A.A.A.—for the benefit of the Midwest and the South and at the expense of the Northeastern farmers.[3] The accusation could not be taken lightly, for not only was the *American Agriculturist* an influential paper in the Northeast but Babcock was acknowledged by the Washington representative of the A.F.B.F. to be one of the most powerful men in farm organization circles and in farm policy-making in the Northeast.[4] Moreover, Babcock's former support of the principle that there should be a national organization for farmers could not be questioned, for it was he who had called the meeting of state farm bureaus at Ithaca in 1919 which resulted in the formation of the A.F.B.F. Among positions which he had held in farm organizations were: secretary of the New York Farm Bureau, general manager of the powerful Grange League Federation in New York state, and assistant chairman of the Federal Farm Board.

There were three major charges which Babcock made against the A.A.A. and the A.F.B.F. First, he charged that the A.A.A. and the A.F.B.F. were controlled by and for the Midwestern and the Southern farmers; the A.A.A. had benefited these two sections at the expense of the Northeast.[5] Specifically, the *American Agriculturist* cited as grievances:

(a) "While the farmers in the Midwest and South have received many millions of dollars in Federal aid, not a single penny has come

---

[3] Howard E. Babcock, "Kernels, Screenings, and Chaff," *American Agriculturist*, March 17, 1934. Babcock regularly contributed articles to the paper under this title.

[4] A.F.B.F., "Minutes of the Executive Committee," *Minutes of the Board of Directors*, June 20-22, 1934.

[5] The sources of most of the grievances cited are editorials in the *American Agriculturist* in 1934. A few minor ones are from articles in the same paper.

to eastern agriculture from the A.A.A. so far as we know, except to a few grain growers."[6]

(*b*) Nearly all of the leaders of the U.S. Department of Agriculture and of the A.F.B.F. came from the Midwest and the South, seldom from the East. "Not in our time has there been an Eastern secretary of agriculture. . . . Never has the East had a President of the A.F.B.F."[7] Secretary Wallace was from Iowa; Chester Davis, head of the A.A.A., also was from the Midwest; and even the A.A.A. milk administrator, A. H. Lauterbach, was a Wisconsin man. Yet New York state at that time ranked fourth in the union for the value of its agricultural products and second in dairy products, while the New York, New England, and Philadelphia milksheds constituted "the greatest fluid milk section in all the world."[8]

(*c*) No action had been taken by the A.A.A. to stabilize milk marketing in the New York milkshed, in spite of agreement upon a code by all the states in this milkshed, and submission of that plan to the A.A.A. months before. The New York state milk control board had done wonderful work, but the trouble was that the New York milk board had no way of controlling the situation in other states. It was "a national and not a state problem."[9]

(*d*) The A.A.A. was taxing Eastern farmers for the benefit of Midwestern and Southern farmers.[10] When the A.A.A. did succeed in raising prices of wheat and corn, the prices of dairy feeds naturally would go up. Thus "dairy farmers are helping to pay the processing taxes to the farmers of the middle west."[11] The bag tax to give cotton growers their benefit payments was expensive to Eastern farmers. So was the attempt by the A.A.A. to cut production of cottonseed meal, thus raising the price of all high-protein feeds.[12]

(*e*) When the A.A.A. caused farmers in the South and West to reduce their production of cotton, corn, or wheat, they would naturally seed down the diverted acres to grass and turn to dairying, thus giving additional competition to Northeastern dairy farmers.[13]

---

[6] Editorial, *American Agriculturist,* January 20, 1934. This was the first issue published after the change in ownership from Morgenthau to the group of four men including Babcock.

[7] *Ibid.,* April 28, 1934.

[8] *Ibid.*

[9] *Ibid.,* January 20, 1934.

[10] Howard E. Babcock, "Kernels, Screenings, and Chaff," *American Agriculturist,* June 28, 1934.

[11] *American Agriculturist,* March 17, 1934.

[12] Howard E. Babcock, "Kernels, Screenings, and Chaff," *American Agriculturist,* March 17, 1934.

[13] *American Agriculturist,* March 17, 1934.

(*f*) Reduction of production in dairying, which might be imposed under the A.A.A., would result in the opening of Northeastern dairy markets to Midwestern producers. The allotment control plan, already applied to cotton, wheat, tobacco, corn, and hogs, was likely to be applied to dairy products. This would only mean that the Northeast would be unable to supply its own markets, and its cities would have to open their markets to "outside milk," that is, to the Midwest.[14] Moreover, it would be unfair if a flat 10 per cent reduction were enforced on Eastern and Western dairymen alike. In every state in the Northeast there were already fewer cows than 20 years before, whereas the number of cows in the Midwest had doubled.[15]

(*g*) There was danger that fluid milk prices would be based on butterfat conditions, since the A.A.A. leaders had the point of view of the Midwest, where most dairymen produced butterfat and not fluid milk. For 50 years before the great milk strike of 1916 the dairymen of the Eastern milkshed had fought the dealers on this principle, and had won the right to have prices based on fluid milk conditions. Now this right might be lost.[16]

Babcock's second major charge was that the emphasis on the A.A.A. program had diverted farmers and farm organizations from the solution of more fundamental problems, such as (*a*) cutting down the cost of food distribution, (*b*) increasing consumption, and (*c*) securing monetary reform—"a permanently honest dollar."[17] Northeastern farmers felt that the processing taxes, for example, were slowing up an increase in consumer buying power, which was what the farmers needed most of all.

The third major charge was that the A.A.A. had become a tremendous bureaucracy, interested mainly in saving its job and saving its face. This bureaucracy would absorb more and more taxes, and use these taxes to influence public opinion.[18]

Another charge, implied in many places, though not stated so explicitly as the others, was that the A.A.A. was based on principles which had no place in traditional American philosophy. Benefit payments were explicitly alleged to be in this category, for: (*a*) they were based on an economy of scarcity, which was abhorrent,

---

[14] *Ibid.*

[15] *Ibid.*, April 28, 1934.

[16] *Ibid.*, March 17, 1934.

[17] Howard E. Babcock, "Kernels, Screenings, and Chaff," *American Agriculturist*, March 17, 1934.

[18] *Ibid.*, March 30, 1935.

(*b*) they were paid only to a small percentage of farmers, and (*c*) they would perpetuate a bureaucracy. Benefit payments were all right, however, as emergency aid to the South and Midwest, where quite possibly they prevented agrarian revolt.[19] Control of production was equally abhorrent, on ethical as well as economic grounds, for "one control leads to another" and "farmers would lose all independence in management."[20] Farmers and A.A.A. employees needing relief should get it, but from relief funds rather than from a processing tax.[21]

Babcock insisted that in attacking the A.A.A. he was not making a political attack, for there were three aspects of the New Deal by means of which, he believed, agriculture had gained enormous benefits. These were: (1) its monetary program, which he believed had been adopted almost exactly from the program of Professor George Warren but which Wallace and his associates were trying to minimize or distort as a factor in bringing improvements; (2) its refinancing of all agricultural operations through the Farm Credit Administration; (3) the hope that lay in its permanent land policy.[22]

Uproar in the A.F.B.F. followed the publication of the following sentences:

Hand in hand with the A.A.A. we find the American Farm Bureau Federation. I believe that I first thought of this organization. I know I called the meeting at which it was formed. Since its inception, I have loyally supported it. Before it was a year old, however, I began to have my doubts about it.

In practice, the American Farm Bureau Federation has always been financially well supported by the east and run by mid-westerners and southerners. On its showing to date, and particularly on its record of late, I am seriously of the opinion that the states east of Ohio and north of the Carolinas should withdraw from the American Farm Bureau Federation. . . .[23]

Members of the A.F.B.F. board of directors from the Eastern states, who were anxious to settle the problem without an open break, believed that 90 per cent of the trouble was economic. The chief difficulty as they saw it was that the price of feed grains purchased (mostly from the Midwest) by Eastern dairymen and poul-

---

[19] *Ibid.*

[20] *American Agriculturist*, March 17, 1934.

[21] Howard E. Babcock, "Kernels, Screenings, and Chaff," *American Agriculturist*, March 30, 1935.

[22] *Ibid.*

[23] *Ibid.*, March 17, 1934.

trymen had gone up by about $4.00 a ton, while the price of dairy products and eggs had not gone up materially. Other increased costs resulted from efforts to protect cotton farmers—the processing tax on cotton goods, the increase in the tariff on jute, and the preferential tax put on paper bags purchased by dairymen and poultrymen.[24]

Some resentment was expressed by Midwestern members at the attack. They were suspicious of political intrigue by the Republican Party, and of the atmosphere created by "politically-minded daily papers" of the East. That the Republican Party was in a difficult situation and Republicans "have been working their heads off to create mistrust" was acknowledged by the New York Farm Bureau president, who, nevertheless, believed that the trouble was essentially economic, not political. The charge that the A.F.B.F. was dominated by Midwesterners and Southerners rankled with President Hearst of the Iowa Farm Bureau, who replied that the Washington office of the A.F.B.F. "has spent more time on getting tariff and other things for eastern agriculture than for western or midwestern agriculture."[25] Earl Smith repeated without pleasure the characterization of himself by Babcock as a man who "doesn't know agriculture east of the Ohio,"[26] and on another occasion Smith made it clear that in his opinion Northeastern dairymen were not farmers but consumers.

Actually, while the conflict flared up in 1934, the roots of it went back to the beginnings of the A.F.B.F. The basic disagreement about the aims of the A.F.B.F., expressed in the organization meetings in 1919 and 1920 (which were described in Chapter II), was never resolved. Once again, in 1934 as in 1919, the Northeast opposed a policy which was understood to mean higher prices for Midwestern feeds, of which Northeastern farmers were heavy consumers.

Opposition to O'Neal's emphasis on the securing of favorable legislation as the chief function of the A.F.B.F. was now added to the Northeast's opposition to the original "business" approach of the Midwest. The central legislative policy of the A.F.B.F. at that period, support of the A.A.A., certainly harmonized much better with Midwestern than with Northeastern interests. Efforts were

---

[24] A.F.B.F., "Minutes of the Executive Committee," *Minutes of the Board of Directors,* June 20-22, 1934.
[25] *Ibid.*
[26] *Ibid.*

continuously made, however, to get things wanted by the Northeast and the West. The administrative report for March 8-9, 1933, states: "There has never been a time in the history of the organization when the president [of the A.F.B.F.] has so constantly given his personal attention to legislative affairs at Washington as during the past three months."[27] Far from considering this fact anything to boast about, President White of the New York federation, the most powerful of the Eastern state farm bureaus, expressed the thought that the A.F.B.F. president should not spend so much time in Washington, but should give more attention to the Extension Service and to membership building in the states. The Northeastern states were particularly displeased because O'Neal, in his preoccupation with affairs in Washington, had deferred a joint conference between Extension Service and Farm Bureau officials.

It is apparent from the following excerpt that White did not look with favor upon the idea that the primary role of the A.F.B.F. should be that of a pressure group. The minutes record:

Mr. White then stated that the president should be at liberty to go to Washington as occasion required, but that he must not be expected to spend his entire time there. He cited his own experience in dealing with the legislature in New York State, remarking that he spent comparatively little time at the Capitol and that frequently when matters of importance came up committees of the legislature sent for him to advise with them. He remarked, "I would rather be in the position of having these men come to me than of going after them." He further remarked, "We should be in a position to help Congress to do things and not attempt to force them."[28]

Moreover, Mr. White stated that "he did not want the status of our organization to be reflected by the idea that our president is just a lobbyist."[29] O'Neal, on the other hand, never thought that there was anything degrading about lobbying for farmers, for he believed in the rectitude of the farmers' cause. Moreover, lobbying openly carried on was part of the democratic process. "I lobbied for this,"[30] he would declare simply about legislation which he was proud of having helped to enact. Nor was O'Neal responsible for inaugurating the policy of Farm Bureau lobbying in Washington, for this had been established in the early 1920's under the administration of the first president of the A.F.B.F. Howard deplored the practice

[27] A.F.B.F., "Administrative Report," *Minutes of the Board of Directors,* March 8-9, 1933.
[28] *Ibid.*
[29] *Ibid.*
[30] O'Neal, personal interview, May 23-24, 1949.

of lobbying but nevertheless felt it necessary for farmers to undertake such activities since pressure groups representing other interests were already entrenched in Washington. The Farm Bureau from the beginning was opposed to secret lobbies, and was in hearty support of the legislation which required lobbyists to be registered. There was one significant difference between the attitude of the Midwesterner Howard and the Southerner O'Neal which perhaps indicates a sectional difference among farmers—while Howard deplored the necessity of lobbying, O'Neal gloried in it.

The Northeastern leaders received some support from the Minnesota and New Mexico farm bureaus in their contention that O'Neal was spending too much time on legislative activities. Mr. Olson, of Minnesota, moreover stated his belief that "President O'Neal is getting too many newspaper headlines at Washington, thereby incurring the jealousy of members of Congress."[31]

The Northeastern fear that O'Neal would neglect relationships with the Extension Service was completely unfounded, for not only was O'Neal an early and late crusader for agricultural education, but he was too astute a politician and too closely in touch with the situation in Alabama not to understand the important political force which the Extension Service wielded in its own right.

Babcock's articles then merely precipitated a conflict which had been smoldering a long time. The fundamental explanation of the threatened revolt is probably to be found in three conditions existing in the Northeast. First, Northeastern farmers generally had not suffered from the depression as much as had Midwestern and Southern farmers, and many Northeastern farmers had actually profited from it. Since the A.A.A. was an emergency measure designed to counter the depression, they naturally might oppose it as unnecessary or harmful. Evidence that the emergency was not so desperate in the Northeast is shown in the figures representing farm mortgage delinquency in 1933. The percentage of mortgaged farms reported delinquent in the Northeast was well below the national average of 45 per cent. Moreover, dairying, which was the source of much of the farm income of the Northeast and represented one-half the gross cash income of farmers in New York state, "had trailed behind" most other enterprises in its descent to the bottom of the depression, which, so far as milk prices were concerned, occurred in January, 1933.[32] A Northeastern member of the board of

---

[31] A.F.B.F., *Minutes of the Board of Directors*, March 8-9, 1933.

[32] R. L. Gillett, "New York Decreasing Milk Production; Conditions Difficult," *The Agricultural Situation*, January, 1934.

directors of the A.F.B.F. admitted that Northeastern dairymen and poultrymen had profited during depression years from the cheapening of grains which they had to purchase for feed.[33] After the A.A.A. was enacted, the situation was reversed, with feed grain prices rising more rapidly than dairy or poultry product prices. According to the Bureau of Agricultural Economics of the U.S. Department of Agriculture, the prices of poultry, eggs, and dairy products went down in 1933 as compared to 1932, while gross income from grains made the greatest increase among important farm commodities in 1933 as compared to 1932. The gross income from grains, including rental and benefit payments, was 86 per cent greater than in 1932, but still only 47 per cent of the 1929 level.[34] Thus the Northeastern farmers as consumers of Midwestern feeds felt exploited by this development, while the Midwestern farmers felt that it was only fair and just.

A second condition unfavorable to the A.A.A. in the Northeast was a political one. Rural New York state, the center of the storm against the A.A.A. and the A.F.B.F., was also a Republican stronghold. So, traditionally, was the agrarian Midwest. But in the case of the Northeast, the economic grievance was aggravated by the belief that a Democratic administration was responsible; whereas Midwestern Farm Bureau leaders, favorable to the economic policy of the A.A.A., maintained that it was a nonpartisan accomplishment.

A third condition conducive to opposition to the A.F.B.F. and the A.A.A. was provincialism among Northeastern farmers based in part on the nature of the markets for Northeastern agriculture. Since the chief farm products of the Northeast were dairy products, poultry, and fruits and vegetables, the markets for which were mainly in the nearby cities, the Northeast did not feel so great an interest in a national program for agriculture, such as the A.A.A., nor so much need of a national organization, as did the Midwest and South, whose markets were either national or international.

Perhaps a cultural factor of stubborn independence, particularly in New England, also contributed—at any rate, A.F.B.F. officials thought so. The organization director of the A.F.B.F. in the Northeastern states believed that one of his chief handicaps was provincialism. In a typical letter he reported to O'Neal:

[33] C. R. White, President of the New York Farm Bureau, to Babcock, March 10, 1934, A.F.B.F., O'Neal Papers (carbon copy).
[34] "Gross Income from Farm Products by Groups of Commodities," *The Agricultural Situation*, March, 1934, pp. 2-3.

The towns visited today border on Plymouth County where I have previously worked and the men visited appear to share the viewpoint of the Plymouth County farmers. It was difficult to make much impression on these men, and it seems incredible that just a few miles can separate farmers with such widely different viewpoints. I can only attribute it to the fact that the farmers who live closer to Boston, and who have an easily accessible market, resent the desire on the part of other farmers, farther away, to share the market, even though they cannot begin to supply Boston's requirements themselves.

Living close to the urban centers, these farmers do not feel the necessity for farm organization to dispose of their products, to secure roads or electricity, and are too nearsighted to see any value in a long time farm program with the objective of proper legislation, tax reduction and cooperative functions. They are extremely provincial in their reasoning, and assume "dog in the manger" attitudes.[35]

In Pennsylvania and New Jersey too, he found difficulty in interesting Farm Bureau people in anything outside their own little circles.[36]

The outstanding Northeastern Farm Bureau leaders, who themselves held the point of view that a national organization and a national program for agriculture were essential to the welfare of the Northeast, sought to overcome this provincialism in their own ranks while not admitting that it was confined to the Northeast. President White of the New York Farm Bureau, for example, wrote to Babcock that he was interested in the great agricultural problems of America as a whole, and wished to get as far from provincialism as possible. "If western men may be called provincial," he said, "I have seen it in our own ranks in the east, and I cannot feel that sectional strife in agriculture will promote the best results."[37] Furthermore, he added, he had never asked the support of the board of the A.F.B.F. for anything for the benefit of Eastern agriculture that was not granted.[38] Another Northeastern leader wrote to O'Neal that it would take some time for the people of southern New England to realize that the A.F.B.F. was not only for Massachusetts and the Northeast but for the country as a whole.[39] O'Neal's reply was that his correspondent should know perfectly well that farmers of the Midwest and the South were for F.D.R.'s

[35] "Report of E. R. Chamberlain, August 17–October 2, 1936," enclosed in a letter from Chamberlain to O'Neal, October 8, 1936.

[36] Letters to O'Neal, August 17, October 2, and October 8, 1936.

[37] C. R. White to Babcock, March 10, 1934, A.F.B.F., O'Neal Papers (carbon copy).

[38] *Ibid.*

[39] George Putnam to O'Neal, May 14, 1936.

farm program—it was just common sense. "Massachusetts folks want to fight about everything."[40] Still another Northeastern state leader found the Connecticut group in a fighting mood in 1935 so far as acreage reduction in potatoes was concerned. They wanted no control themselves, but would have been glad to see the potato acreage in Maine reduced. Furthermore, he said, "New England growers do not fully understand the principles back of these marketing agreements and are inclined to look upon the situation as an opportunity to increase production at the expense of those situated at a distance from our markets."[41]

In addition to the criticism in the Northeastern farm press, an intraorganization scandal contributed in a minor way to the flare-up of old conflicts. It was revealed at a Senate hearing on ship subsidies that the secretary of the A.F.B.F., M. S. Winder, who was a nonelective officer, was being paid by a certain Mr. Van Petten, who in turn received a commission from the Asphalt Association (or the Asphalt Institute) for a publicity campaign concerning secondary roads which was carried on through the publicity channels of the A.F.B.F. Neither Sam Thompson, President of the A.F.B.F. at the time the contract was negotiated, nor the board of directors, nor the existing officers were aware that Winder was receiving such money until the revelation in the Senate hearing. The employment of Winder, and of the information director as well, was terminated, and O'Neal took the opportunity to get the board of directors to give the president a clear authority over the employed staff.[42]

The publicity about the Senate investigation came out just after the New York Farm Bureau had widely advertised Winder as a speaker at a series of county farm bureau meetings. The Farm Bureau was considerably discredited, and there was much criticism

[40] O'Neal to Putnam, April 6, 1936.

[41] S. McLean Buckingham to O'Neal, February 3, 1935.

[42] It was revealed to the meeting of the board of directors of the A.F.B.F. in which the Winder affair was aired that staff members had been used to going directly to the members of the board to secure support for some policy which they wanted to put across, and had taken the attitude that they were not responsible to the president but to the committee of the board and to the resolutions of the annual meeting. Further, it was revealed that there had been a tendency of some of the staff to look to the executive secretary, Mr. Winder, as the responsible head, rather than to the president. Legal Counsel Kirkpatrick commented that the practice of designating the secretary as "executive secretary" had grown up over the years, though there was no provision for it in the bylaws. A.F.B.F., *Minutes of the Board of Directors,* December 7-8, 1933; A.F.B.F., "Minutes of the Executive Committee," *ibid.,* October 29, 1933.

of the A.F.B.F. among farmers in the Northeast, even from "the substantial old boys who had been promoting the organization since its beginning."

O'Neal and the board of directors of the A.F.B.F. were much disturbed by the crisis in the Northeast in 1934. Yet they could not interfere directly to attempt to straighten things out, for the decentralized structure of the A.F.B.F. was such that interference from national headquarters would have only worsened the situation. The dilemma was clearly pointed out by O'Neal when he brought the matter before the board for discussion: "I believe fundamentally in state rights and probably it is not the business of the American Farm Bureau Federation to interfere with the East but it fundamentally affects the Farm Bureau and if it is possible to do anything, the American Farm Bureau is perfectly willing to do it. . . . It does seriously affect the national organization and we would not want to be in the position of defending one section against another and we might sit down together and counsel together."[43]

O'Neal's skill in getting people "to counsel together" was demonstrated on this occasion. It must have been a major factor in achieving his goal of maintaining agricultural unity. Other tactics which O'Neal demonstrated in dealing with the Northeastern situation were: to try to keep conflicts from coming out into the open; to play up the matters on which there was agreement; to ensure that everyone got something which he wanted; and to call upon the loyalty and duty of men to a cause that transcended their own interests, at the same time making clear to them that it was to their interest to do so. O'Neal's conviction that he was working for a just and righteous cause must have given him an influence which his mastery of the skills and intricacies of power politics alone could not have done, even though he gloried in the latter as in a game in which he knew all the arts and held a strong hand.

C. R. White, President of the New York Farm Bureau, the most powerful farm bureau in the Northeast and the one in which the trouble centered, was apparently not under personal attack in his home state for his membership on the board of directors of the A.F.B.F. As has been indicated previously, he took the lead for the Northeast both in explaining its grievances to the board of directors and in counseling on action. Director Putnam, one of the grand old men of the A.F.B.F., whose influence in the Northeast was greater than his position as president of the New Hampshire

---

[43] *Ibid.,* June 20-22, 1934.

Farm Bureau would suggest, saw no tendency to revolt in either New Hampshire or Vermont. He believed that the trouble centered in New York, New Jersey, and possibly Massachusetts.[44] President Spargo of the New Jersey Farm Bureau reported that members had threatened to depose him because of the fact that he had stood "four-square on the national program."[45]

White proposed to call a meeting in the Northeast to clear up the situation. He was opposed to confining such a meeting to "our own little group," but instead thought it necessary to include "these men" (presumably Babcock and other critics), the Extension people, and the Grange.[46] Spargo agreed that "the Big Show has to come off" and if the A.F.B.F. tried to stop it, it would be too bad for the Farm Bureau in New Jersey.[47]

It seems that O'Neal had brought up the Northeastern situation for discussion before the board of directors of the A.F.B.F. with the object of persuading White of the unwisdom of calling such a general meeting. Putnam had tried to induce O'Neal to invite Babcock to this board meeting, but O'Neal "thought it wasn't the thing to do."[48] O'Neal's opposition to the idea of a general meeting in which the conflict would be publicly aired was probably based on his agreement with the opinion of the Washington representative, Chester Gray, that "it would wash Farm Bureau linen in public, which none of us desire to do and it would be a hammer conference to knock and to criticize rather than for the purpose of helping."[49] Putnam did not wish New Hampshire involved in a general meeting which might drag New Hampshire into the "mess," but offered to come down to New York and New Jersey to speak "if I can defend you fellows."[50] White was inclined to think he would have a conference with Babcock and his supporters before the general meeting.[51]

If White had insisted upon going ahead and calling the type of general meeting which he first proposed (i.e., one which would have brought the conflict into the open for general discussion), there was nothing which the A.F.B.F. could have done to stop him. However, the A.F.B.F. board of directors adopted a motion which

---

[44] *Ibid.*
[45] *Ibid.*
[46] *Ibid.*
[47] *Ibid.*
[48] *Ibid.*
[49] *Ibid.*
[50] *Ibid.*
[51] *Ibid.*

stated that the executive officers of the national federation would
be glad to participate in a meeting called by one or more of the
Eastern state farm bureaus, and that "disaffection in the Farm
Bureau should not be an issue at the conference," which should be
"for a general discussion of northeastern agriculture, the purpose
being to see if activities cannot be broadened to help northeastern
agriculture."[52] As Earl Smith commented, "Nothing takes the place
of a conference when you are careful who attends with reasonable
control of the program."[53]

The conference was duly held, and the crisis which had threatened was averted. In fact, the membership of the Northeastern
farm bureaus continued to expand during the New Deal period, although not at so fast a rate as in some other sections.

It was not so much the conference, but three forces fundamentally more conducive to unity, which probably explain why the
Northeastern region failed to withdraw from the A.F.B.F. in 1934.

First, there was a strong tradition of loyalty among the leaders
which had been built up over the years. Honest expression of disagreement was treated with exquisite courtesy on the board of directors of the A.F.B.F. The loyalty of a director to the principle of
a national organization and a national program for agriculture was
not impugned when, as representative of his state or region, he dis-
agreed with, or failed to support, specific policies adopted by the
national organization. Concrete evidence of the loyalty of state
leaders to the A.F.B.F. in spite of their own lack of enthusiasm for
the A.A.A. was given in the Northeastern conflict. When certain
New York counties voted to secede from the A.F.B.F. but wished
to remain members of the New York state federation, the New York
state leaders pointed out to them that in order to belong to the state
organization they must also contribute their dues to the American.[54]

Second, the A.F.B.F. supported two policies about which the
Northeast was particularly keen. These were: (*a*) the monetary
policy advocated by Professor George Warren of Cornell, and (*b*)
co-operation with land-grant colleges and the Extension Service in
agricultural education. The A.F.B.F. specifically endorsed Professor Warren's "commodity dollar" scheme, and used the Farm Bureau's influence in Washington to get it embodied in national legislation. New York state and Vermont were the chief Farm Bureau

[52] *Ibid.*
[53] *Ibid.*
[54] E. S. Foster, General Secretary of the New York Farm Bureau, to O'Neal,
October 20, 1936.

advocates of the Warren "commodity dollar" plan, although currency stabilization by some method was a fundamental policy of the
A.F.B.F. as a whole. In maintaining and increasing federal appropriations to the federal-state Extension Service, the national Farm
Bureau Federation played a role which was an important comple-
ment to that played by the state farm bureaus in their state legislatures. In 1935, for example, the secretary of the New York state
federation, in expressing his state's appreciation of the "splendid
work" done by O'Neal and the A.F.B.F. Washington representative
on legislation which increased appropriations for land-grant college teaching, extension, and research, even went so far as to express the opinion that "you two are largely responsible for the
success of this measure. . . ."[55]

If sometimes the Northeast complained that the A.F.B.F. was
emphasizing other policies to the neglect of the monetary policy
and the Extension Service, O'Neal was privately not too much disturbed, for he was convinced that without the help of the A.F.B.F.,
Northeastern farmers were politically impotent to get what they
wanted. Looking back in 1939, he wrote of the New York Farm Bureau:

> The fact is, I have often been astonished in my fifteen years that I have
> been on the Board or one of the officers, to see in what a splendid way
> they have co-operated and the high record of their membership through-
> out the years. As you know too, I have been personally very fond of their
> leaders. They have a great state organization. Confidentially, one of the
> biggest difficulties with them is that they have but little influence on their
> Congressmen and Senators. This is, I guess, due largely to the fact that
> they are afraid of being charged of being politically-minded, and they
> haven't had the broad approach and aggressive fighting qualities of a
> number of our other great state Farm Bureaus. I wish they had this. It
> would have made the task so much easier for us in the national congress
> all these years. Even on their monetary program, on which they bank so
> heavily, they have had practically no votes. This of course, is just my ob-
> servation to you.[56]

The third fundamental force by which unity was maintained was
an implied "deal" or bargain between the Northeast and the Midwest, backed by an implied threat to Northeastern agriculture from
the Midwest. The "deal," though not overtly expressed, was understood to be that the Northeastern farmers could have milk marketing agreements which would give them a monopoly in the milk
markets of the Eastern cities if the Midwest could have higher

---

[55] Foster to O'Neal, July 16, 1935.
[56] O'Neal to J. F. Porter, President of the Tennessee Farm Bureau, November
22, 1939.

prices for its feed grains. An editorial by Clifford Gregory in the *Prairie Farmer* makes clear what the alternative was: "For years after the depression of 1920, and particularly since 1929, Eastern dairymen have profited because they could buy feed for less than it cost Middle Western and Southern farmers to produce it. This situation is being corrected. . . . They [Midwestern farmers] must get fair prices, or else they will go more heavily into dairying themselves, and then Eastern farmers will have real reason to think their shirts have been stolen."[57]

By 1936 it appeared that complete harmony had been restored between the Northeast and the A.F.B.F. In June of that year the Northeastern regional conference of presidents and secretaries sent a telegram to O'Neal endorsing the entire program of the A.F.B.F. which was being presented to the platform committees of the Democratic and Republican national conventions, and calling special attention to the necessity of adopting the monetary plank.[58] The actual situation, however, was not quite what it appeared, for the endorsement of the total program was partly the result of a maneuver. The events back of the telegram were described, with great glee, by Putnam of New Hampshire in a letter to O'Neal:

No doubt you received the wire giving the endorsement of the North-east to the program you were presenting to the convention resolutions committee. Of course Arthur Packard [of Vermont] and the New York boys wanted special mention of the commodity dollar. It is rather interesting how this came about. On Tuesday morning when we were in session, Mr. Packard made a proposal that we wire the resolutions committee at Cleveland urging the adoption of the commodity dollar proposal in the Republican platform. Buckingham of Connecticut was presiding over our session and he hesitated for a moment, and no one having seconded Packard's motion, I made the point that it would be embarrassing to our directors in Cleveland if we were to endorse only one of the various proposals that were being made to the committee. Mr. King [of New York] realized the situation and we talked about it for a minute or two, and I said I was perfectly willing that we emphasize the commodity dollar but I felt that we should include approval of the whole Farm Bureau program. Benjamin of Pennsylvania made a motion that we send such a telegram.

This put the Massachusetts boys and the commodity dollar boys on the spot until someone seconded Benjamin's motion, which was unanimously adopted. I got a good deal of kick out of this because as you must realize.

---

[57] *Prairie Farmer*, April 14, 1934.

[58] Telegram from S. McLean Buckingham, chairman of the presidents' and secretaries' conference of the state farm bureaus of Vermont, New Hampshire, Connecticut, Massachusetts, New Jersey, Pennsylvania, and New York, to O'Neal, June 9, 1936.

it places the northeast region behind the entire Farm Bureau program, and I can go down to Philadelphia with the rest of you boys and say, "The Northeast is behind it."[59]

Once again, as in 1919, fundamental differences were only ameliorated, not resolved. Northeastern leaders continued to deplore the primary emphasis on legislation which characterized the A.F.B.F. under O'Neal's administration. They complained that the narrowing of the program to one that was largely legislative had meant the abandonment of the once "splendid transportation department, cooperative marketing, and so forth."[60] Crop control, which was basic to both the A.A.A. and to O'Neal's legislative policy became more, rather than less, unacceptable to Northeastern farmers. O'Neal, realizing this, ceased trying to win them to the production control program, for he could see that there was no use.[61] In 1937 the secretary of the New York Farm Bureau reported that never had there been such strong opposition to the A.F.B.F. as then existed, and that the primary issue was crop control, to which many farmers strongly objected.[62] Southerners, who were becoming the strongest advocates of production control, were of the opinion, however, that production allotments were no more monopolistic and restrictive than was the device of marketing agreements, which the Northeast admitted it had found very helpful, especially for their dairy farmers.[63] Lots of farmers in New York, so the secretary of that state federation declared in 1938, were coming to have the opinion that the A.F.B.F. was being run by the U.S. Department of Agriculture, "which was just a mouthpiece for Henry Wallace's schemes."[64]

That the Northeastern states remained within the A.F.B.F., even while many of them at the same time opposed the major national policy then endorsed by that organization, was a triumph for the diplomacy of Ed O'Neal, for the loyalty of their local leadership, and for the decentralized structure of the federation. On this occasion the cohesive power of compromise overcame the divisive threat of secession.

---

[59] Putnam to O'Neal, June 12, 1936.

[60] A.F.B.F., *Minutes of the Board of Directors,* December 12, 1936. An Eastern delegation presented its viewpoint to the board at this meeting.

[61] O'Neal to Foster, August 18, 1936.

[62] Foster to O'Neal, November 24, 1937.

[63] "Suggestions of the Northeastern Conference to the Directors and Committee on Resolutions of the A.F.B.F., 1939," A.F.B.F., O'Neal Papers.

[64] Foster to O'Neal, December 21, 1938. Actually, the New York farmers could not have been more wrong in this instance, for the break between Henry A. Wallace and the A.F.B.F. had already begun by 1938.

CHAPTER VI

Membership Is Power:
The Southern Membership Drive

"Membership is power, that is all there is to it," said Charles Hearst, Vice-President of the A.F.B.F., in 1934.[1] The gist of power politics in a democratic society is summed up in these blunt words. A keen awareness of this principle lay at the base of the organizational strategy of the A.F.B.F. leaders during the critical period following the establishment of the A.A.A.

No other major farm organization was as enthusiastic a supporter of the A.A.A. as was the Farm Bureau. Yet its leaders soon detected a threat to their organization in the possibility that the production control committees of the A.A.A. might become organized into another farm organization, or into a political machine. The first time this possibility was discussed by the A.F.B.F.'s board of directors was at its meeting on June 20-22, 1934. From then on, the A.F.B.F. was alert to forestall any such move. Since the A.F.B.F. itself had originated in association with another government agency—the Extension Service—it was readily aware of the precedent for such a development.

What shocked the A.F.B.F. into action was the so-called "farmers' march on Washington" which took place on May 14, 1935.[2] This march seems to have been a mass movement aroused by what was felt to be danger to the A.A.A. brought on by the attack of the textile interest against the processing tax. Certainly if the movement were the result of an organized plan, it was not planned by the A.F.B.F. The farm bureaus had conducted mass meetings and ral-

[1] A.F.B.F., *Minutes of the Board of Directors*, December 14, 1934.
[2] Cf. Lord, *The Wallaces of Iowa*, pp. 449-50. Lord describes the gathering in Washington as "as sort of postdated Populist outing."

lies in states and counties to arouse the farmers to fight for the retention and strengthening of the A.A.A. But the A.F.B.F.'s interpretation of the events that followed was that the farmers were so thoroughly aroused that the idea of the march began among the farmers themselves, started by one or two leaders among the A.A.A. production control committees in the South. The A.F.B.F. did not recommend the march, in fact was fearful of it, but once the movement gained momentum, O'Neal was anxious for the state farm bureau leaders to step in and take charge of it and guide it.[3] The Farm Bureau feared not only that the cotton control committeemen in the South, where the Farm Bureau was weak, might use the march to set up another farm organization, but that the dairy group, "who are now getting on the bandwagon, may try to run away with the show and capture all the credit for what has been done by putting on a 'big show' at Washington."[4]

As to the action which the Farm Bureau should take in this situation, there seems to have been a difference of opinion between O'Neal and Chester Gray, the A.F.B.F.'s Washington representative, whom O'Neal had left in charge of arranging things.[5] Gray must have sent out a letter to state farm bureau leaders advising them to discourage the movement as mob action which would do no good, for O'Neal telephoned him on May 6, begging him not to send any more letters like the one of May 3. "I was distressed," said O'Neal, "because you are turning it over to the other fellow. They will ride to glory."[6] O'Neal had himself sent telegrams to the state farm bureaus telling them to keep the leadership.[7] While he did not suggest that they organize delegations to Washington, he thought that in some cases it might be desirable, and in any case he urged them to keep the leadership of activities in their states.[8] Gray's view was: "We generally get in a few effective men who know how to work instead of making it a mob affair."[9] Moreover,

---

[3] A.F.B.F., "Administrative Report," *Minutes of the Board of Directors,* June 5-6, 1935; O'Neal to R. W. Blackburn, President of the California Farm Bureau, May 3, 1935.

[4] W. R. Ogg, Acting Secretary of the A.F.B.F., to O. O. Wolf, President of the Kansas Farm Bureau, May 4, 1935. Ogg later became director of research of the A.F.B.F., in which capacity he served as Washington representative.

[5] O'Neal to Blackburn, May 3, 1935.

[6] Telephone conversation between O'Neal and Gray, May 6, 1935, A.F.B.F., O'Neal Papers (typescript).

[7] *Ibid.*

[8] Telegram from O'Neal to 33 state farm bureaus, May 6, 1935 (typescript).

[9] Gray to O'Neal and the executive committee, May 6, 1935.

Gray believed that if the press notices were correct in stating that the cotton commodity control committees were sponsoring the march, the A.F.B.F. might not be able to take charge.[10] Replies to O'Neal's telegram were received from at least two state farm bureau presidents, assuring him that they were leading delegations from their states—Arkansas and Kansas.[11]

Chester Gray was present at some of the meetings in Washington on May 14 held by the "marching farmers." He estimated that at least 3,000 out of the 4,000 farmers present came from the South and the rest came from the Midwest, and he believed that the convention definitely was sponsored by the county and state A.A.A. committees.[12] Very few Farm Bureau leaders were in charge of their state groups, he believed, although Farm Bureau people were scattered throughout most of the state groups. Almost no mention was made by speakers of the role of farm organizations in securing the A.A.A., except by Secretary Wallace and possibly by Chester Davis, whom Gray did not hear. President O'Neal and a representative of the Farmers' Union were introduced, but given no opportunity to speak.[13]

O'Neal believed that the only thing that prevented the A.A.A. production control committees from setting up their own organization at this meeting in Washington was the presence of a number of Midwestern Farm Bureau leaders there, who headed it off by saying they could not go along with the South on this, as they "had a dominant farm organization in the Farm Bureau in this section [the Midwest] which was serving the needs of the people."[14] Moreover, Farm Bureau leaders believed that both the A.A.A. administrator, Chester Davis, and Secretary Wallace (in accordance with a promise allegedly made) were at that time carefully refraining from using their influence to promote a new general farm organization, federally controlled.[15]

---

[10] *Ibid.*

[11] Telegrams to O'Neal from J. F. Tompkins, President of the Arkansas Farm Bureau, May 6, 1935, and O. O. Wolf, May 8, 1935.

[12] Gray to O'Neal and the executive committee, May 15, 1935. Lord, *The Wallaces of Iowa*, p. 449, says there were 4,500 farmers and 100 county agents present.

[13] Gray to O'Neal and the executive committee, May 15, 1935.

[14] O'Neal to Wilmer Mills, President of the Louisiana Farm Bureau, May 21, 1935. See also similar statements in A.F.B.F., "Administrative Report," *Minutes of the Board of Directors,* June 5-6, 1935.

[15] O'Neal to R. W. Brown, President of the Missouri Farm Bureau, May 16, 1936. See also "Joint Meeting of the A.F.B.F. Executive Committee and the Executive Committee of the Extension Service, June 22, 1934," A.F.B.F., "Minutes of the Executive Committee," *ibid.,* June 20-22, 1934.

That the situation was, nevertheless, considered by Farm Bureau officials to be very critical is indicated by the following statement:

The organization of more than 3 million contract signers [i.e., farmers co-operating with the control program of the A.A.A.] constitutes either the greatest opportunity in the history of the Farm Bureau to strengthen its organization, or the greatest potential threat to the Farm Bureau's leadership and prestige. These 3 million farmers are organization conscious. . . .

If the Farm Bureau can enlist even one third of these 3 million contract signers as members of the Farm Bureau, it would firmly establish the Farm Bureau as the dominant organization to speak for agriculture. On the other hand, if we fail to enlist in the Farm Bureau these contract signers, it probably will be very difficult if not impossible, to prevent the establishment of another farm organization out of the framework of the control committees and contract signers, particularly in the states where there are no Farm Bureaus or where our Farm Bureau organizations are small in membership. . . .[16]

One way of obviating the danger was suggested in the recommendation that county farm bureaus be the local administrative units for the A.A.A.[17] Even this measure would not have taken care of the situation in areas where the Farm Bureau was so weak as to be virtually nonexistent.

While an intensive membership campaign was proposed for all four regions, it was in the South that the danger and the opportunity for the Farm Bureau were thought to be greatest. Ninety-four per cent of the contract signers under the A.A.A. were estimated to be in the South and Midwest,[18] but whereas the Farm Bureau was already strong in the Midwest (where 65 per cent of the total A.F.B.F. membership in 1933 was located), it was weak in the South. Since President O'Neal was himself from Alabama, he was both particularly interested in promoting the farm bureaus in the Southern states and particularly well qualified to do so.

According to a plan suggested in the administrative report to the board of directors, wherever practicable A.A.A. production control committees were to be invited to serve as organization committees to organize a farm bureau in their local communities. In many instances it was expected that the chairman of the production control committee would become the president of the county farm bureau, and the members of the committee would

---

[16] A.F.B.F., "Administrative Report," *ibid.*, June 5-6, 1935.
[17] "Joint Meeting of the A.F.B.F. Executive Committee and the Executive Committee of the Extension Service, June 22, 1934," A.F.B.F., "Minutes of the Executive Committee," *ibid.*, June 20-22, 1934.
[18] A.F.B.F., "Administrative Report," *ibid.*, June 5-6, 1935.

constitute the board of directors of the county farm bureau. They would be asked to serve, "not in their capacity as committeemen, but as leaders in whom farmers have confidence."[19] Thus the complaint of production control committeemen that they had no organization through which they might share in local and national policy-making would be met, without the necessity of their forming a separate and perhaps competing farm organization.[20]

While the aim of the membership drive in the South was to capture the organization-consciousness of the A.A.A. beneficiaries, the actual policies used were more dependent upon co-operation with another agency, the Extension Service—the traditional ally of the Farm Bureau. Alabama was the base from which the Southern membership drive was launched, and Dr. L. N. Duncan was O'Neal's chief adviser on Extension Service relationships. Dr. Duncan, who had been O'Neal's mentor in the early Farm Bureau days in Alabama, was, until 1937, both president of the land-grant college in Alabama and director of the Alabama Extension Service. After 1937 he continued in the former position but gave up the latter under pressure (resulting from factional differences within both the Extension Service and the Farm Bureau). While there was no direct legal tie between the Extension Service and the Farm Bureau in Alabama, Dr. Duncan's Extension Service had originally sponsored the organization of the Farm Bureau in that state, and his county and district agents continued to give it leadership and support, without violating the letter of the True-Howard agreement of 1921 (which forbade the Extension Service to engage in direct membership solicitation for the Farm Bureau). Dr. Duncan's assistance to O'Neal in the Southern membership drive consisted not merely of advice but also took more practical forms, two in particular being invaluable. (1) He used his influence informally with Extension directors in other Southern states, and offered to help O'Neal to make contacts with them.[21] (2) By granting leave of absence to members of the staff of the Alabama Extension Service, he made available to O'Neal some experienced organizers to spark the Farm Bureau's Southern membership drive.[22] Two men

---

[19] A.F.B.F., "Suggested Plan of Special Membership Campaign," *ibid.*

[20] *Ibid.*

[21] Duncan to O'Neal, January 24 and June 8, 1935.

[22] O'Neal to Duncan, June 8, 1935; Duncan to O'Neal, November 2, 1935; O'Neal to Duncan, December 23, 1935; telegram from O'Neal to R. G. Arnold, June 16, 1936; telegram from Arnold to O'Neal, October 26, 1936; telegram from Arnold to O'Neal, March 13, 1936; telegram from O'Neal to Arnold, March 13, 1936.

whom Duncan lent to O'Neal were R. G. Arnold, district supervisor for the Alabama Extension Service, who acted as chief Southern organizer for the Farm Bureau; and Charles J. Brockway, an Alabama county agent, who acted as secretary of the North Carolina Farm Bureau during the reorganization phase in 1936.[23]

Illustrative of Dr. Duncan's assistance is the letter which he wrote to Dean I. O. Schaub of the North Carolina State College, April 6, 1936, a carbon copy of which was sent by Duncan to O'Neal. The complete letter is as follows:

My dear Dean Schaub:

We have all been delighted at the progress that you good people in North Carolina are making with your farm organization.

It has been a pleasure for Mr. Arnold and the other members of the staff to assist with this matter. Mr. O'Neal and all the other mutual friends are most appreciative of what is being done there in North Carolina.

Some headway is being made in some of the other Southern states, and it would be very fine if we could have a systematic and standard growth of this type of organization throughout the South.[24]

The relationship between Dr. Duncan and O'Neal was not, however, that of assistance from one side alone. Mutual benefit was expected. For instance, a telegram from Duncan to O'Neal in 1937 states: "Your co-operation is respectfully requested in getting President Roosevelt to approve Senate Bill 1052 which provides funds badly needed for Extension work."[25] This, of course, was simply a request that the Farm Bureau should lobby for the Extension Service.

Unhappily for the Farm Bureau, Extension directors were not all so co-operative as Dr. Duncan in Alabama. In some states they were indifferent, in others actually hostile, to the idea of promoting the Farm Bureau. In such cases it was always O'Neal's way to try to win them by persuasion, but if persuasion failed, then he did not hesitate to bring pressure or the threat of pressure. To the Louisiana Farm Bureau president who complained that he could not get co-operation from the Extension director, O'Neal wrote: "Sometimes we do have to force co-operation from the Extension fellows."[26] He added, however, that co-operation works both ways, and that the Farm Bureau in Louisiana would have to straighten out its "business services," as had been done in Alabama, before

---

[23] "Resolution of the North Carolina Organization Committee," enclosed in a letter from E. F. Arnold, county agent, to O'Neal, February 24, 1935.

[24] Duncan to Schaub, April 6, 1936.

[25] Telegram from Duncan to O'Neal, August 26, 1937.

[26] O'Neal to Wilmer Mills, March 14, 1936.

it could demand co-operation from the Extension Service on a mutually agreeable basis.[27]

Since the state Extension Services were largely state-controlled, although supported in part by federal funds, it was necessary for O'Neal to know the local situation intimately in each state. In those states in which another general farm organization was strong and the Farm Bureau weak, the Extension Service was sometimes considered unco-operative by Farm Bureau officials. Outside the South, in Pennsylvania, for example, the Farm Bureau organizer considered that the opposition of the Grange prevented the Extension Service from being more co-operative.[28] In some states O'Neal realized that the local political situation was such that neither persuasion nor pressure by a national organization could influence the Extension Service. For instance, O'Neal conceded that in Louisiana Huey Long's opposition might be a formidable obstacle to co-operation by the state Extension Service with an independent farm organization. With this in mind O'Neal wrote the Louisiana Farm Bureau president: "You most certainly have to be careful because Senator Long might light on you with all four feet. It is a wonder he hasn't already."[29] In Georgia the political situation under Governor Eugene Talmadge was not considered favorable to co-operation between the Extension Service and the Farm Bureau, probably for the same reason.[30] Later, however, there was a hint that if a Georgia Farm Bureau leader whose political associations were advantageous could be secured, the Extension Service might subsequently be brought into line, although it could not be used to spark the organization drive. In other states, sometimes an Extension director who was an independent and strong-willed individual might be the chief obstacle, as the A.F.B.F. organizers reported to be the case in North Carolina. It was in this last type of situation, however, that the opportunity and the challenge for the Farm Bureau were considered greatest.

In 1939 the possibility that activities carried on by the Extension Service on behalf of the Farm Bureau might be drastically curtailed was raised by the so-called "Alabama incident." This issue was precipitated by the publication in the *Washington Daily News*

---

[27] *Ibid.*

[28] "Report of E. R. Chamberlain, August 17–October 2, 1936," enclosed in a letter from Chamberlain to O'Neal, October 8, 1936.

[29] O'Neal to Wilmer Mills, May 21, 1935.

[30] O'Neal to General R. E. Wood, President of Sears, Roebuck and Company, December 14, 1935. There are also other letters of the same general tenor.

on June 1 of a letter from a county agent in Alabama, R. L. Griffin, which had been sent out, under Extension Service franking privileges, to farmers in his area, advising them that their A.A.A. checks were awaiting them in his office, and urging them to join the Farm Bureau.[31] It was clearly implied in the letter that the Farm Bureau had been responsible for the benefits received by farmers from the A.A.A.

The Alabama letter appeared to be a flagrant violation of the rule (which had been laid down in the True-Howard agreement in 1921 and confirmed in a letter of Secretary of Agriculture Henry C. Wallace in 1922) that county agents might aid the farming people in a broad way to organize Farm Bureau and other co-operative organizations, but must not themselves conduct membership campaigns.

O'Neal was alarmed for fear that the Alabama incident would cause the incumbent Secretary of Agriculture, Henry A. Wallace, to send out a letter to county agents forbidding them to participate in any Farm Bureau promotional activities whatsoever, and he attempted to dissuade Wallace from such a course. O'Neal described his efforts in letters to the Farm Bureau's Washington representative, and to the director of the Alabama Extension Service. According to O'Neal, he spent an hour and a half with Wallace, at which time "I read him extracts from his father's letter to Extension workers, dated August 25, 1922. I told him, frankly, I thought it would be a very serious mistake for him to send out a similar letter at this time."[32] Just how strongly O'Neal put his case is not certain, but he says: "I pointed out that such a letter would be dynamite now and the Farm Bureau today wouldn't agree to any such policies set forth in that letter. . . . I have insisted . . . that the incident is closed."[33]

O'Neal was not successful in persuading Wallace to consider the incident closed. However, Wallace did apparently confine himself to sending a memorandum to Federal Extension Director C. W. Warburton in which, rather than laying down a general ban, he pointed out two specific abuses. Wallace began this memorandum by saying that apparently some co-operative Extension Service workers were not aware of their relationship to the U.S. Depart-

[31] Block, *op. cit.*, p. 25.
[32] O'Neal to W. R. Ogg, Washington Representative of the A.F.B.F., November 2, 1939.
[33] O'Neal to P. O. Davis, Director of the Alabama Extension Service, November 11, 1939.

ment of Agriculture. Their attention, he continued, should be called to the fact that if they engaged in certain practices, their appointments with the Department of Agriculture would be terminated, and federal funds would be withdrawn from their salaries. The two practices specified were: "(1) use of the franking privilege in mailing letters soliciting membership in a local farm organization, and (2) making arrangements or permitting arrangements to be made for the cashing of agricultural conservation payment checks for the express purpose of deducting dues for a farm organization in the county extension office or at other places in the county where these checks were being delivered to farmers."[34]

Apparently nothing much came of the "Alabama incident" except for some intensification of criticism of the special relationship between the Extension Service and the Farm Bureau. Federal Extension Director Warburton made the standard request for an investigation by the state director, in this case P. O. Davis of Alabama. Davis reported that he had reprimanded the county agent, Griffin, who had "admitted [that] in a moment of enthusiasm he had done something contrary to policy."[35] However, the newspaper publicity, together with Wallace's memorandum, probably curbed such enthusiasm and had a restraining influence on future overt membership activities on the part of Extension workers.

To secure the co-operation of A.A.A. officials was second only in importance to securing the co-operation of the Extension Service. The A.F.B.F.'s plan in each state was to approach first the Extension Service and A.A.A. officials in order to try to establish friendly contacts with them.[36] To direct the strategy, or at least to advise on it, O'Neal thought it most important to have someone who had both the confidence of the Extension Service and a familiarity with the setup and personnel of the A.A.A. cotton control committees.[37] He thought that Walter Randolph might be the man for this "very keenly diplomatic mission," and he asked Dr. Duncan to discuss this matter with Randolph and his associates.[38]

Walter Randolph had been virtually reared in the Alabama Extension Service, in which he had held various positions, such as

---

[34] "Memorandum for Dr. Warburton, November 10, 1939," A.F.B.F. files (copy).
[35] Block, *op. cit.*, p. 26.
[36] A.F.B.F., "Suggested Plan of Special Membership Campaign," *Minutes of the Board of Directors*, June 5-6, 1935.
[37] O'Neal to L. N. Duncan, June 8, 1935.
[38] *Ibid.*

administrative assistant to Dr. Duncan, and editor for the Extension Service and Experiment Station. He had also been connected with the Alabama Farm Bureau, as its director of information (by co-operative arrangement with the Extension Service) at the time when O'Neal was president of the Alabama Farm Bureau. Later Randolph served as its executive secretary. Afterward, when the A.A.A. came in, he had been associated with this agency in various capacities, once for instance on the state A.A.A. committee, for another period as a senior agricultural economist for the A.A.A. in Washington, and eventually as administrative officer in charge of the A.A.A. in Alabama.[39] In his home state of Alabama, Randolph had a reputation for both integrity and a phenomenal memory.[40] Until he became president of the Alabama Farm Bureau in 1940, he could not assume generalship of the Southern Farm Bureau forces, but it is quite clear from correspondence in the O'Neal Papers that his advice was sought and respected.

In 1933 Alabama was the strongest Farm Bureau state in the South, but its membership was only 2,590. Illinois alone had a membership about four times that of the whole Southern region (36,420 as compared to 9,473 for the South). The Midwestern region as a whole contained about 65 per cent of the membership, as well as probably a larger proportion of the wealth of the A.F.B.F. In the South, elsewhere than in Alabama, there were no real farm bureaus except in the border states of Tennessee, Virginia, Kentucky, and Maryland, where there was still a vestige of strength. O'Neal expected that North Carolina and Texas would be the key states in the membership drive to build up a new Southern Farm Bureau.[41] Greatest success was actually achieved in North Carolina and Georgia, and there was considerable success in Arkansas too.

[39] The details of Walter Randolph's career are taken from a letter from P. O. Davis to the Secretary of Agriculture, Henry A. Wallace, August 21, 1937, A.F.B.F., O'Neal Papers (carbon copy).

[40] Stories of Randolph's remarkable memory were told the author in Alabama in 1949. That integrity was not always considered a convenient quality is indicated in a letter from (name withheld) to O'Neal, November 5, 1940. It reads in part: "There was only one statement Randolph made to me that I did not like. He said that he never in his life had gone against his own well thought-out conscientious scruples on any question, to which ———— and I both told him it was a noble idea to have conscientious scruples, but when loyalty to a great cause like the farm bureau, or to one's friends and co-workers was involved, damn the scruples and vote with your group." So far as the author knows, O'Neal respected Randolph's conscientious scruples.

[41] O'Neal to L. N. Duncan, June 8, 1935.

A description of the membership drive in North Carolina will therefore serve as a case study in the methods used, demonstrating that success depended upon (1) capitalizing upon the A.A.A., (2) cordial relations with the Extension Service, and (3) flexibility based upon "inside" knowledge of the local situation. The last consideration was a most important one, for in some states, as has been noted, the local situation was such that even with expert knowledge of where the difficulties lay, local forces were sometimes beyond the control of the A.F.B.F.

In North Carolina it was chiefly among A.A.A. tobacco control committeemen that the Farm Bureau was originally formed, early in 1936.[42] Only production control committeemen were invited to a meeting, apparently in February, 1936, at which a temporary organization was set up.[43] The organizational work was started in 30 counties in the eastern part of the state, centering around the town of Greenville,[44] where the chief crop was tobacco, with peanuts an important secondary crop. Cotton was important in some of these counties, but the true cotton belt counties were not among them. The fear that tobacco production controls might be lost after the Supreme Court's decision in January, 1936, declaring large portions of the A.A.A. to be unconstitutional, probably was the chief stimulant to the organization of a farm bureau, through which it was hoped new federal legislation providing for production controls could be ensured. The original resolutions adopted by the North Carolina organization meeting in February point to this conclusion, for they first pledge co-operation with a federal program for 1936, and second, call for further restrictions in the acreage of tobacco, cotton, and peanuts.[45]

The A.F.B.F. organizers found the North Carolina Extension Service "hard to move."[46] Dr. Duncan of Alabama had promised to

---

[42] A North Carolina Farm Bureau had existed during an earlier period, but had disappeared.

[43] *Ibid.* A list of 28 of these counties was sent to O'Neal by Charles J. Brockway, Acting Secretary of the North Carolina Farm Bureau, in March of 1936. These were: Wilson, Pitt, Greene, Lenoir, Craven, Bertie, Edgecombe, Martin, Duplin, Washington, Camden, Beaufort, Pasquotank, Nash, Gates, Currituck, Chowan, Hertford, Carteret, Franklin, Halifax, Jones, Perquimons, Warren, Wayne, Northampton, Onslow, and Johnston.

[45] "Original Resolutions Adopted by North Carolina, February, 1936," A.F.B.F., O'Neal Papers. They are signed by a committee consisting of W. W. Eagles, Edgecombe County; G. T. Scott, Johnston County; and Jno. R. Carroll, Pitt County. Apparently these men were the organization committee.

[46] Charles J. Brockway to O'Neal, March 31, 1936.

contact Dean Schaub, Extension director in North Carolina,[47] but Schaub was an independent individual who could not be hurried. The organizer for the Farm Bureau thought that Schaub was afraid of the governor of the state, and of the local Grangers too.[48]

It seems likely that it was not so much fear of the governor or of the Grangers that kept Dean Schaub from being enthusiastic about pushing the organization of the Farm Bureau, as it was simply that he felt that the Extension Service had more important work to do. The Farm Bureau's organizer wrote to O'Neal that the county agents were busy holding soil conservation meetings, and although he was "chiseling in" wherever they would let him, their program was too full for much Farm Bureau work. Otherwise he found the entire Extension Service an intelligent group, very considerate and co-operative, the trouble with them being that they all wanted to "wait awhile." He was finding it hard to take O'Neal's and R. G. Arnold's suggestion to let the Extension Service advise, for they would not be hurried. "I am having more trouble educating the county agents than the farmers," was the gist of his complaint. "The farmers are 'raring' to go. But most of the county agents are scared or indifferent. . . . I can't get these damned county agents to send in their *reports*. They are about as sorry as Alabama County Agents when it comes to making reports. If we had L. N. Duncan over them, we could get 100,000 members within 30 days."[49]

The conversion of Dean Schaub to the Farm Bureau movement was reported a little over a month later. It was believed to have been brought about by the big Raleigh "Cramton Bowl" meeting of about 6,000 farmers in regard to the tobacco compact issue. This meeting was conceived and organized by Brockway, working in close co-operation with J. E. Winslow, President of the North Carolina Farm Bureau, and E. F. Arnold, the local county agent in Greenville, North Carolina.[50] After the meeting, it seemed to the president of the North Carolina Farm Bureau and to the Southern organizer that Schaub had seen the light.[51]

The North Carolina Farm Bureau leaders planned to make the impending low price for tobacco that fall the paramount issue in the campaign, and they felt sure that they could get the co-opera-

---

[47] L. N. Duncan to I. O. Schaub, April 6, 1936, shows that Duncan carried out his promise. A.F.B.F., O'Neal Papers (carbon copy).

[48] Charles J. Brockway to O'Neal, March 31, 1936.

[49] *Ibid.*

[50] R. G. Arnold to O'Neal, May 4 (or 6), 1936.

[51] *Ibid.*

tion of farm leaders in the tobacco section of North Carolina and of the entire Extension Service in the campaign in the next few months.[52]

O'Neal was much relieved by the seeming success of the campaign, for while the A.F.B.F. had gambled "pretty heavily" in North Carolina, he now felt it was "historic." "If we can just do the same thing in Arkansas and Mississippi," he said, "we will really make a heavy start in spreading the Alabama plan throughout the South."[53]

It was felt that North Carolina was the most important state in the Union to the Farm Bureau cause, other than Illinois, for it represented an "entering wedge to a great uncolonized empire for farm organization."[54]

The Southern organizer was highly pleased over the success in North Carolina, but somewhat skeptical of the continuing fidelity of Dean Schaub. To offset possible defection, the Southern organizer suggested that O'Neal get in touch with J. B. Hutson, tobacco chief of the A.A.A. in Washington, and have a tobacco conference called in Washington with Schaub, Hutson, O'Neal, and the North Carolina Farm Bureau officials present.[55]

O'Neal was reassuring in his reply:

Mr. Hutson is very much our friend and will do everything he can to help us. He has shown this by his co-operation all along in our work in North Carolina.

Director Schaub went about as far as a fellow could go with me in our conference in Washington. Frankly, he pledged the co-operation of himself and his workers in building a Farm Bureau and, although he stated he had his own way of approach, knowing him as long as I have, I know that he is pretty determined about this way.[56]

Since Brockway was only on leave of absence from the Alabama Extension Service, a man had to be found for the position of permanent secretary of the North Carolina Farm Bureau. For this position O'Neal recommended that "a local man and old county agent is best."[57]

Three years later, in spite of the auspicious beginning, the A.F.B.F.'s organization director for the Southern region considered the North Carolina Farm Bureau a patient "sick unto death." The secretary chosen according to O'Neal's formula—"local man and old

---

[52] *Ibid.*
[53] O'Neal to R. G. Arnold, May 6, 1936.
[54] R. G. Arnold to O'Neal, May 8, 1936.
[55] *Ibid.*
[56] O'Neal to R. G. Arnold, May 11, 1936.
[57] *Ibid.*

county agent"—was excellent so far as lobbying activities were concerned. He made 33 trips to Washington during one year for tobacco and peanut legislation, but he was reported to know nothing of organization and to have no interest in it.[58] The membership campaign in North Carolina was also adversely affected by the British withdrawal from purchasing in the American tobacco markets in 1939.

The man found to take the place of the former county agent as the central figure in the North Carolina Farm Bureau was R. Flake Shaw, operator of a diversified farm in Guilford County. Shaw was considered to be the only available man who could make the North Carolina Farm Bureau a statewide organization, instead of the regional one it had been up to this time. Previously, the organization and its activities had been almost exclusively confined to a group of tobacco and peanut counties in the eastern part of the state. Shaw's county of Guilford, however, was in the middle, or Piedmont, section of the state, where tobacco was important but where diversified agriculture was typical. His only weakness was considered to be that, like all other farmers who take over a professional job after age 50, he had no training for the particular job— in this instance, that of a professional organizer. Consequently, he could not insist on signing farmers on the dotted line, and he shied away from asking farmers to do things for themselves. However, the director of Extension, Schaub, and the state A.A.A. administrator, E. Y. Floyd, were both said to be enthusiastically for him. It was felt that they might "wet-nurse" him through to success.[59]

Two other centers of influence in North Carolina agricultural circles need to be noted, for they were a part of the local situation which the Farm Bureau organizers had to take into account. One was Clarence Poe, editor of the *Progressive Farmer,* which still carried on much of the tradition of its crusading founder, Colonel L. L. Polk (onetime prominent leader in the Populist Party). Poe had been Polk's protégé. Living just outside the state capital, Raleigh, and editing what was probably the most influential farm journal in the Southeast. Poe played an important part in farm policy-making, a fact of which O'Neal was quite aware. O'Neal advised the North Carolina Farm Bureau organizers to make contact with Poe, whom he considered his friend although Poe and O'Neal were opposed on many issues. Poe was particularly interested in

---

[58] R. G. Arnold to O'Neal, November 2, 1939.
[59] R. G. Arnold to R. W. Blackburn, October 10, 1940.

protecting the interests of the small farmers, as his letters to O'Neal (to whom he appealed for support in this matter) indicate. When the Farm Bureau took up the fight against the Farm Security Administration, Poe supported Farm Security. Nevertheless, O'Neal and Poe had many interests in common—among them agricultural education and the improvement of Southern agriculture in particular. Accordingly, the two leaders in Southern agriculture tried in a friendly fashion, even though sometimes in disagreement, to influence each other on matters of agricultural policy.[60] O'Neal wrote his North Carolina organizer that Poe was not nearly so Grange-minded as might be supposed, and that his support was worth seeking. The only farm organization already well established in North Carolina, though not powerful, was the Grange. After the organization of the Farm Bureau in the state, the *Progressive Farmer* seems to have given impartial support to both farm organizations.

Another center of influence in North Carolina farm affairs, this one considered to be a source of opposition, was the state commissioner of agriculture. At the time of the second organization drive in North Carolina, that of 1939-40, the Southern commissioners of agriculture were believed by the A.F.B.F. to be conducting a lobby in Washington, the main object of which was to win support for the Cooley-Bailey marketing bill, which provided for Congressional appropriations to state commissioners of agriculture for marketing research.[61] Further, the lobby of the Southern commissioners of agriculture was supposed by the A.F.B.F. to be working through the Southern governors,[62] and in conjunction with the Grange. The Grange, for its part, was suspected of trying to build up a government-agency ally such as the A.F.B.F. possessed in the Extension Service.

The North Carolina commissioner of agriculture, Kerr Scott, was reported by President Winslow of the North Carolina Farm Bureau to be working to get Secretary of Agriculture Wickard to come to North Carolina to make a speech, as part of the plan to get the Cooley-Bailey bill passed. As Scott was not only alleged to be working for this bill but was a leading Granger as well, such a meeting held in his section of the state, it was believed, would be injurious to the Farm Bureau cause. Winslow therefore urged, instead, that

---

[60] Several such letters exchanged between Poe and O'Neal are to be found in A.F.B.F., O'Neal Papers.
[61] W. R. Ogg to O'Neal, August 15, 1940.
[62] Ogg to O'Neal, August 21, 1939.

the A.F.B.F. try to get the Secretary of Agriculture to come to North Carolina to speak in a Farm Bureau section—that is, in Pitt County.[63] At a later period, Kerr Scott, like Clarence Poe, supported the Farm Security Administration when the Farm Bureau was fighting it.

The reorganization and the intensive membership campaign in 1940 resulted in the transformation of the North Carolina Farm Bureau from the stillborn infant of 1936 to the strong state organization of which the A.F.B.F. officials had dreamed. Perhaps the very quality about the new executive, Flake Shaw, which the A.F.B.F. organizer considered to be a weakness, enabled him to win the confidence of the plain farmers of North Carolina and to succeed where the more high-powered organizers had failed. The reopening of the tobacco markets and the surging prosperity of tobacco farmers (for whom Shaw subsequently became a recognized spokesman on the A.F.B.F. board of directors), the high wartime prices for other crops and the feeling among farmers that organization would help them to protect these prices in the expected postwar deflation, and the cordial relationship with the Extension Service and with the A.A.A.—all were factors that probably help to explain the success of the Farm Bureau drive in North Carolina.

In Georgia also, outstanding success was achieved in the membership campaign, although not until 1941, when the state Farm Bureau was reorganized. When it was suggested that the A.F.B.F. advance the money for three months' salary for the new chairman of the state organization committee, O'Neal was eager to make the arrangement, but felt that he had to have the support of Earl Smith before committing A.F.B.F. funds to the project. "I got plenty of money in the fund," said O'Neal, "but hesitate to go on and do it on my own."[64] Earl Smith wished to know if they would pay back. O'Neal replied no, but pointed out that a similar arrangement had been used in six or seven states—for example in Mississippi, Texas, Arkansas, and North Carolina. Earl Smith thought that this was "an awful big cost anywhere—much less Georgia."[65] He also believed that local people had to help themselves (the Midwestern point of view)—the A.F.B.F. could not do it for them. Nevertheless, he told O'Neal to use his own judgment and that he would

---

[63] Winslow to Ogg, October 16, 1940.

[64] Telephone conversation between O'Neal and Smith, June 11, 1941, A.F.B.F., O'Neal Papers (typescript).

[65] *Ibid.*

support him.[66] Apparently the plan succeeded, for the Georgia Farm Bureau grew to become the largest in terms of membership in the South.

In Arkansas too, where cotton and rice were the important crops, the Farm Bureau experienced a remarkable development, from no paid-up members in 1933 (the same situation as in North Carolina) to 30,582 in 1943. This state provides an instance of how the local political situation might affect a Farm Bureau membership drive. A crisis occurred in Arkansas in 1940, when it was alleged that the governor of the state set out to destroy the Farm Bureau, and in the fight obtained the co-operation of the A.A.A. and of the Extension Service.[67] In these circumstances it was pointed out to Arkansas farmers that they could not expect President Roosevelt, Secretary Wallace, the Extension Service, or even the Lord himself to come down and build them a permanent organization. They had to do it themselves.[68] Apparently they did, for the Arkansas Farm Bureau became strong and firmly established. Perhaps the fact that the governor was not re-elected helped.

Considerable success was thought to be taking place in Mississippi too, but this later proved to be somewhat illusory. Protests within the A.F.B.F. by Midwesterners over the second-rate non-voting membership allowed to Negroes in Mississippi led to a dispute within the national federation as to the number of members Mississippi should claim in computing the number of voting delegates to which the state was entitled at the annual general meeting of the national federation. This probably accounts for the sudden drop in the membership figures from 36,601 in 1946 to 15,389 in 1947. During the period of this study, however, Ransom Aldrich from Mississippi continued to be one of the four Southern members on the A.F.B.F. board of directors.

Texas was a source of grave disappointment, the trouble there being, from the A.F.B.F. point of view, that Texas was plagued by too many "voluntary movements,"[69] that is, farm organizations not planted by the A.F.B.F. O'Neal bitterly asserted in 1938 that "the co-ops had killed the Texas Farm Bureau after it had spent all its membership funds in helping them."[70] By 1948 a measure of suc-

---

[66] *Ibid.*
[67] R. G. Arnold to O'Neal, May 14, 1940.
[68] Arnold to R. W. Blackburn, May 19, 1940.
[69] O'Neal to Ralph Snyder, Kansas Farm Bureau leader, September 3, 1935.
[70] O'Neal to J. F. Porter, November 4, 1938.

cess had been achieved in Texas, but it still lacked the strong Farm Bureau membership that the smaller states of Alabama, Arkansas, Georgia, Kentucky, and North Carolina had.

Meantime, the older Southern state farm bureaus had increased their membership many times over. Alabama, for example, increased from 2,590 members in 1933 to 41,014 in 1943 and 61,667 in 1948. But by 1948, Georgia with 73,000 and North Carolina with 67,554 members were both ahead of Alabama. The "Alabama plan" had succeeded remarkably well in these states.

North Carolina and Georgia had been characterized, even from pre–Civil War days, by family-type diversified farms rather than by a staple-crop, plantation type of agriculture. It would seem, therefore, that the Farm Bureau Southern membership drive, although at first aimed at capturing the producers of the A.A.A. basic crops, eventually found its strength and success in states where more general and smaller-scale farming predominated. However, tobacco was probably the magic key which unlocked North Carolina to the Farm Bureau.

When Roosevelt was inaugurated in 1933, the South was the weakest of the four regions in the Farm Bureau. In all four regions the increase in membership during the New Deal period was striking, but the percentage increase in the Southern region was by far the greatest. In 1935, the year in which the intensive membership campaign was inaugurated, the Southern region rose from fourth to third place in membership, and in the next year to second place, being led by the Midwestern region only. The Farm Bureau usually flourished in times of prosperity and dwindled in times of depression, but prosperity alone does not explain the disproportionate increase in Southern membership.

The initial impetus for the Southern drive undoubtedly came from the desire to capitalize on the first A.A.A. and to prevent the formation of a rival organization. Solid success was not achieved, however, until after 1940.

Still, it would not be valid to conclude that the A.A.A. made the Southern Farm Bureau, for the co-operation of the Extension Service and a flexible strategy based on astute knowledge of local situations were at least equally important. A broader point of view would include consideration also of the fact that just as the New Deal and World War II were times of rising farm prices and rapidly rising membership in farm organizations, these were equally periods of rising wages for industrial labor and rapidly rising membership in labor unions.

CHAPTER VII

Harmonious Relationships

"Certainly, more than any Secretary of Agriculture that I have ever
known, Secretary Wallace has conferred and advised with the
farm organizations' leaders, particularly the Farm Bureau," wrote
O'Neal in 1936 to a fellow Farm Bureau leader.[1] This statement
leaves no doubt that in 1936 the Farm Bureau considered that it was
on eminently satisfactory and particularly close terms with Franklin
D. Roosevelt's Department of Agriculture. To be consulted by the
Administration, to have its advice heeded in the making of agricultural policy, was the Farm Bureau's concept of an ideal relationship
between farmers and the government. Practically everything about
both Roosevelt and the Department of Agriculture pleased O'Neal
in the early 1930's. Even Tugwell's ideas for a "planned agriculture"
O'Neal thought were splendid.[2] Later it became apparent that
O'Neal had understood neither Tugwell nor his ideas.

Henry A. Wallace and O'Neal probably did understand each
other quite well during the early New Deal period, or at least they
understood each other's ideas. Wallace himself has said that he and
Ed O'Neal worked very closely all during the thirties.[3]

An explanation by M. L. Wilson clarifies the relationship. Wallace
and the Department made their own decisions, said Wilson, but
Wallace would *listen* to the views of others, including farm organizations. In the early period, added Wilson, Farm Bureau
leaders had the *preferred* position among farm organizations to
whom Wallace would listen. The Grange ranked next and the
Farmers' Union came third.[4] Of course no official ranking was made.

---

[1] O'Neal to R. W. Brown, President of the Missouri Farm Bureau, May 18,
1936.
[2] O'Neal to Henry A. Wallace, January 5, 1934, A.A.A. Papers, National
Archives.
[3] Wallace, personal interview, August 27, 1959.
[4] Wilson, personal interview, August 18, 1959. Mr. Wilson corrected the

In the files of the correspondence of the Secretary of Agriculture are various invitations (and acceptances) for consultation between Wallace and the Farm Bureau leaders. Sometimes the requests were made by the Secretary of Agriculture, sometimes by O'Neal, and apparently sometimes the arrangements were made by Clifford Gregory.[5] Any request by O'Neal for a conference usually began with the words "Earl and I." Sometimes they met in the U.S. Department of Agriculture offices; sometimes they met in Chicago. There was nothing clandestine about these meetings. The same privilege was extended to other farm organizations, though perhaps not so frequently. In the Secretary's files there are also letters from Farm Bureau leaders recommending various people for jobs. The Department of Agriculture did not hesitate to turn down any such requests for persons who were not qualified, but it seems likely that the Department went to considerable trouble to find a job for which Mrs. O'Neal's nephew *was* qualified.

The relationship between the A.F.B.F. and the Roosevelt administration during the early New Deal was in fact so close that the Department of Agriculture may well have begun after two or three years to feel crowded by it. In 1935, for example, when Chester Davis, then Administrator of the A.A.A., protested against making a speech over the radio at O'Neal's request, O'Neal brushed aside his protests in a kindly but firm manner: "You have to talk, dear buddy."[6] A check of the record shows that Davis did talk.[7]

author's use of the word "predominant" to describe the position of the Farm Bureau.

[5] For instance, on April 17, 1940, Mr. Gregory advised that he had arranged for a conference with Secretary Wallace and the executive committee of the A.F.B.F. at the Sherman Hotel on April 28 (Correspondence of the Secretary of Agriculture, National Archives). At this time Gregory may have been attempting to reconcile Wallace and the Farm Bureau.

[6] Statement made by O'Neal in one of three separate long-distance telephone calls which are recorded on the matter between him and Chester Davis in one day (April 6, 1935, A.F.B.F., O'Neal Papers, typescript). Davis' protest was that if he went on the air on the National Farm and Home Hour to blast the enemies of the A.A.A. processing tax, the National Broadcasting Company people said that, since this was a controversial matter, they would have to give the same amount of time on the Farm and Home Hour to the enemies of the A.A.A. This the N.B.C. was reluctant to do because hitherto the Farm and Home Hour had been devoted to educational interests. O'Neal assured Davis that he was mistaken and that he would himself go down to New York to straighten out the matter with the N.B.C. "Frankly," said O'Neal, "I feel that you owe it to the American people. This thing is very serious. You owe it to tell the facts. You can do it in such a way not to be offensive and Sidney sent out releases, so you have to talk, dear buddy." The Sidney referred to is probably Sidney Rubinow, Director of Information for the A.F.B.F. Later

In a more important matter, however, Davis showed himself to be quite capable of withstanding pressure from O'Neal while still maintaining a cordial relationship with him. In 1935 there was considerable dissatisfaction in the Midwest over the administration of the corn-hog program of the A.A.A. Farmers were said to feel that their veracity had been impugned in certain orders from Washington and from state administrators of the A.A.A. The executive committee of the A.F.B.F. therefore urged that the A.A.A. accept the certified statements of farmers and of county allotment committees on hog population (as a basis for county and individual quotas and claims) instead of stressing the estimates and opinions of economists and legal specialists.[8] Chester Davis' reply to O'Neal was: "I do not believe your committee seriously intends to ask us to approve counties in blank unless county committees have done everything possible to remove inaccurate claims."[9]

Such incidents reveal that increasing pressure on the Department of Agriculture by the Farm Bureau might in time nullify the advantages to the Department of its political support.

With urban labor, as well as with the Administration, the A.F.B.F. continued to have generally harmonious relations until the late 1930's. Just as the early New Deal measures had depended upon the combined support of labor and agriculture, so the support of urban labor was important to the Farm Bureau in gaining new legislative victories after the Supreme Court's invalidation of the first A.A.A. in 1936.

Harmony with labor and with the Administration was particularly important to the Farm Bureau at this time. Not only did organized business continue to be hostile, but by the period 1936-39 the relative unity that had existed in 1933 among the "Big Five" farm organizations had been fractured, and even Congress—the usual stronghold of the Farm Bureau—was at times antagonistic.

On January 6, 1936, the Supreme Court's decision in the Hoosac Mills case, by which much of the A.A.A. was invalidated, created

---

in the day Davis informed O'Neal that "they" were attempting to separate him from his official capacity by putting him on as guest speaker.

[7] On April 13, 1935, Chester Davis appeared as guest speaker on the A.F.B.F. program over the National Farm and Home Hour. *A.F.B.F. Official News Letter*, April 16, 1935.

[8] Telegram from the A.F.B.F. executive committee to Henry A. Wallace, June 21, 1934, A.A.A. Papers, National Archives.

[9] Telegram from Davis to O'Neal, June 25, 1934, *ibid.* A note penciled on the telegram indicates that Davis gave a more extended answer to O'Neal orally in conference in Washington.

a crisis perhaps as much for the A.F.B.F. as for American agriculture. The Farm Bureau had proudly claimed the paternity of the A.A.A., and now that this favorite offspring was declared illegitimate, the prestige of the Farm Bureau and its position of leadership among agricultural organizations was threatened. On the day of the invalidation of the A.A.A., O'Neal's immediate reaction is revealed in a telegram to Earl Smith, the gist of which was: Apparently the Supreme Court decision "knocks out" the whole A.A.A. program; the Farm Bureau must take action immediately. The action then suggested by O'Neal was of a somewhat panicky nature—namely, that farm bureaus should call county mass meetings within the next 48 hours to shower Congress and the President with telegrams demanding immediate legislative action to assure economic equality to farmers, even if such legislation required amending the Constitution. "Imperative that Farm Bureau retain leadership in this fight," was O'Neal's concluding exhortation.[10]

Upon calmer reflection, or perhaps upon the advice of calmer colleagues, O'Neal ceased to talk in terms of amending the Constitution, for, as he discovered, the Farm Bureau organization itself was too much divided upon the desirability of such a course.

Once again, as in 1933, Secretary Wallace invited Farm Bureau and other farm organization leaders to come to Washington to consult with him on new farm legislation. His telegram of January 7, 1936, to Ed O'Neal reads: "Will you come to Washington to attend National Conference of Farm Leaders here on Friday & Saturday January tenth and eleventh to consult with me on agricultural program in the light of Supreme Court decision. Please include such of your executives as you see fit. Expenses of one representative will be reimbursed."[11]

The Soil Conservation and Domestic Allotment Act was quickly enacted, in February, 1936, as a stopgap measure to replace the A.A.A.[12] There was some difference of opinion, however, among

---

[10] Telegram from O'Neal to Earl Smith, January 6, 1936.

[11] Telegram from Wallace to O'Neal, January 7, 1936, A.A.A. Papers, National Archives.

[12] Under the Agricultural Adjustment Act of 1933, the government had attempted to control production of farm commodities by offering benefit payments to farmers for reducing their acreage of the basic crops. It was hoped that this sort of regulation could be justified under the commerce clause of the Constitution. When the Supreme Court declared this act to be unconstitutional, the Soil Conservation and Domestic Allotment Act was passed, depending for its constitutionality upon the powers of the federal government to promote the general welfare. (In this case it was argued that the conservation of national

the supporters of the act of 1936 as to whether it was primarily a soil conservation measure or a means of continuing production control under the guise of conservation. It was hoped that both purposes would be achieved. Within the Department of Agriculture there was apparently considerable feeling that soil conservation should be the primary objective, with production adjustment a by-product.[13] O'Neal was a staunch supporter also of soil conservation, but his primary interest was that the act of 1936 should be a means of continuing the practice of production control which had been inaugurated under the first A.A.A.

Among various differences between the act of 1933 and the act of 1936 was one which had an important bearing on the relationship between the A.F.B.F. and urban labor. The act of 1936 provided no means equivalent to the processing tax, which had been a central feature of the act of 1933, for financing the soil conservation program. Soil conservation payments would have to depend on Congressional appropriations from the federal treasury. Since conservation of soil resources was generally a more popular theme in urban circles than among rural people, it probably was not anticipated that there would be any extreme difficulty in securing such appropriations. In such matters, however, the support of urban labor would prove indispensable.

The Presidential election of November, 1936, gave farmers a chance to express their verdict on the New Deal program for agriculture. "The Middle West is the great question mark," wrote Clifford Gregory in an article entitled "The Farmer in the Coming Political Campaign."[14] According to Gregory's predictions, Southern farmers would of course remain Democratic, while not much defection from traditional Republican ranks was to be expected of Northeastern farmers. It was the Midwestern farmers whose vote could not be counted upon with certainty by either party. Gregory believed that Midwestern farmers were well satisfied with the agricultural policies of the Roosevelt administration, with one important exception. This was the foreign trade program, symbolized by the reciprocal trade policy, which was not popular with Midwestern

---

soil resources was a legitimate means to that end.) Instead of being paid for not producing crops, farmers were paid for planting certain soil-conserving crops, and later plowing them under to enrich the soil.

[13] U.S. Department of Agriculture, *Agricultural Adjustment Administration, 1937-38* (Washington: Government Printing Office, 1939), p. 11.

[14] Carbon copy in A.F.B.F., O'Neal Papers.

farmers. These farmers, indeed, did not wish liberalization of foreign trade policy but rather wished further restrictions on competing agricultural imports such as blackstrap molasses (which was
competitive with corn in the production of industrial alcohol).
Weighing the gratitude of Midwestern farmers to President Roosevelt for his domestic farm policy against their opposition to his
foreign trade policy, Gregory concluded: "The import issue will
gain some farm votes for the Republicans in the pivotal Middle
Western states, but probably not enough. On the other side of the
balance is the high regard of these Middle Western farmers for
President Roosevelt and his agricultural assistants, and gratitude
for what they have done. And this, as things look at this time, seems
to be the decisive factor."[15]

The position taken by Earl Smith in the campaign was a significant
indicator of the way the Midwest would go, both because he was
the outstanding Midwestern Farm Bureau leader, and because, like
the majority of Midwestern farmers, he was Republican by tradition. Earl Smith's comments in the July, 1936, issue of the *Illinois
Agricultural Association Record* could leave little doubt that he
found the Democratic platform the more satisfactory on farm
policy.[16] He deplored the Republican platform's criticism of the
Agricultural Adjustment Act. He gave much of the credit for the
rise in farm prices to the Democratic administration, which, he declared, had adopted the agricultural policies recommended by "organized agriculture" (i.e., the Farm Bureau) in 1933.

Even more important, to Earl Smith, than the party or the party's
platform was the candidate's stand on agricultural issues. In an
address entitled "Lest We Forget," which Earl Smith gave at the
Iowa state fair in October, 1936, just prior to the election, he re-
minded Midwestern farmers that during the campaign of 1932,
Roosevelt had promised the farmers of America that if elected he
would call together "the chosen leaders of American agriculture"
(i.e., the leaders of agricultural organizations), and if they would
agree on a program, he would approve it, provided it was economi-
cally sound, administratively feasible, and self-supporting.[17] "I pay
tribute to President Roosevelt for keeping his word," declared
Smith.[18] No agricultural leader would be likely to make such a

---

[15] *Ibid.*
[16] *Illinois Agricultural Association Record,* July, 1936, p. 23.
[17] Earl C. Smith, "Lest We Forget," *ibid.,* October, 1936, pp. 4-5. The words
in quotation marks are Earl Smith's.
[18] *Ibid.*

speech during the closing weeks of the Presidential campaign unless he favored the candidate whom he thus praised.

When the Midwest voted for Roosevelt in 1936, O'Neal was both relieved and jubilant. His correspondence makes clear that he had felt a sense of responsibility for the vote of Midwestern farmers. For the Farm Bureau to have failed "to deliver the votes" to the candidate who had been "the most sympathetic friend" they had ever had in the White House would have been interpreted as a sign of impotence on the part of the farm organization. The pro-Roosevelt vote could be interpreted as rank and file support of Farm Bureau leadership. Moreover, O'Neal genuinely believed at this time that the salvation of American agriculture depended upon the re-election of Franklin D. Roosevelt. In retrospect, the anxious concern over how the Midwestern farmers would vote in 1936 appears to have been completely unnecessary, in view of the ease with which Roosevelt was swept back into office with the electoral votes of every state in the union except two. But nobody knew until the votes were counted. The Administration itself made special efforts to win the uncertain Midwestern farm vote. When M. L. Wilson, Assistant Secretary of Agriculture, went out to that region immediately prior to the election to survey the political possibilities informally, he found the popularity of Henry A. Wallace riding particularly high.[19]

In addition to the election of Roosevelt, O'Neal took a particular interest in 1936 in the campaign for re-election of Senator George Norris of Nebraska. While Senator Norris and the A.F.B.F. had been antagonists in the pre–New Deal struggle over the issue of the disposition of Muscle Shoals, O'Neal bore him no grudge.[20] Rather, O'Neal held Norris in high regard. This was no public pose, for

---

[19] Wilson, personal interview, August 29, 1959.

[20] Senator Norris favored government ownership and operation of the power facilities at Muscle Shoals. At that stage the A.F.B.F. was opposed to government operation, and proposed instead various schemes for leasing Muscle Shoals to private entrepreneurs or to a co-operative representing organized agriculture. The main object of all of the Farm Bureau's proposals was to ensure the production of quantities of cheap fertilizer, and thus to break the hold of the fertilizer trusts on the farmers. Senator Norris thundered against turning over the great national resources at Muscle Shoals to private enterprise. It was Senator Norris' basic concept which was most nearly adopted when the Tennessee Valley Authority was established under the Roosevelt administration. But O'Neal was always as enthusiastic about the T.V.A. as if it were his own idea, and indeed he considered that if it had not been for the A.F.B.F.'s long struggle to have Muscle Shoals developed by one agency or another, there would have been no T.V.A.

O'Neal took part in some behind-the-scenes maneuvers to aid the re-election of Norris in 1936.

In that election campaign Norris was in a very precarious position, as the vote would be split. He was running as an Independent against both Republican and Democratic opponents. The secretary of the Nebraska Farm Bureau, E. T. Winter, wrote to O'Neal saying that he and other Nebraska Farm Bureau officials had agreed with Senator Norris' secretary on a plan by which they could best help the senator. They would ask a Nebraska farmer to write to O'Neal asking his opinion of Senator Norris' services to agriculture. Then they would arrange for wide circulation of his reply.[21]

Subsequently, in reply to a telegram from Mr. Howard Eastman of Walthill, Nebraska,[22] O'Neal wrote a glowing letter about Norris, which begins: "I feel there is no man in the United States Senate who has been more outstanding in the long fight for social and economic equality for agriculture."[23] On November 3, 1936, Winter wrote O'Neal that his letter had been published in a labor magazine of some 50,000 to 60,000 circulation,[24] and in a great many country weeklies; parts of it had been quoted in daily newspapers; and some of it had gone on the radio.[25]

Insofar as the O'Neal Papers indicate, it was exceptional for O'Neal to take so direct and personal a part in the election of congressmen or senators. His special admiration for Senator Norris is expressed in a letter to the Farm Bureau friend in whom O'Neal confided most freely: "You know, Joe, what the Farm Bureau needs to develop are real . . . fighting leaders. This, I have been begging for a long time. We ought to have men like George Norris, who think, eat, and sleep their cause, so that they won't be denied when they get up and fight."[26]

Though Norris had been a Republican and was then an Independent, he was more genuinely a New Dealer than were many Democrats. O'Neal's endorsement of him was, in part at least, an expression of profound satisfaction with the New Deal program.

---

[21] Winter to O'Neal, October 9, 1936.

[22] Telegram from Eastman to O'Neal, October 12, 1936.

[23] O'Neal to Eastman, October 13, 1936.

[24] This was probably *Labor* (Washington, D.C.), a national weekly published by the Railway Workers of America. O'Neal wrote the manager of this magazine, Edward Keating, sending him a carbon copy of the letter to Eastman. O'Neal to Keating, October 13, 1936.

[25] Winter to O'Neal, November 3, 1936.

[26] O'Neal to J. F. Porter, August 25, 1937.

While the vote in the Presidential election of 1936 indicated that the Soil Conservation and Domestic Allotment Act which had been passed earlier in the year was acceptable stopgap legislation to farmers, by 1937 the A.F.B.F. was working strenuously for new general farm legislation to supplement if not to replace this law. In this aim the Farm Bureau was in harmony with the Roosevelt administration, which for some time had been seeking to develop farm legislation of a more enduring character than either the emergency-born Agricultural Adjustment Act of 1933 or the crisis-generated Soil Conservation and Domestic Allotment Act of 1936.[27]

By 1937 it was clear that O'Neal's hope that production control could be effectively achieved under the Soil Conservation and Domestic Allotment Act of 1936 was not being fulfilled. Even under the more stringent regulations of the first A.A.A., the success of production control had been doubtful. Now that the legislative lid was practically off, the production of bumper crops in 1937 was facilitated. The reappearance of normal weather conditions after the severe droughts of 1934 and 1936 provided a propitious situation. Other explanations probably entered in, but whatever the reason, the index of agricultural production as a whole in 1937 reached a new high. In contrast, farm prices began a downward trend in 1937, and in 1938 they dropped very sharply.[28] Whether or not the large crops were responsible for the low prices, many farmers thought that they were. Industrial recession also occurred in the fall of 1937, and this was certainly related to the fall in agricultural prices, although whether primarily as cause or effect is debatable.

Although the Roosevelt administration agreed that new farm legislation was necessary in 1937 and 1938, its reasons for doing so differed somewhat from those of the Farm Bureau. The Soil Conservation and Domestic Allotment Act of 1936, while possessing enduring merit as a soil conservation measure, was not comprehensive enough to fulfill the aims of the Administration for a permanent agricultural policy. Secretary of Agriculture Henry A. Wallace was particularly eager to incorporate the "ever-normal granary"

[27] The Administration's viewpoint is stated in U.S. Department of Agriculture, *Agricultural Adjustment Administration, 1937-38*, pp. 97-98.

[28] On the size of crops and prices, see *ibid.*, pp. 98-99, and U.S. Department of Agriculture, *Agricultural Adjustment Programs, 1933-41* (Washington: Government Printing Office, 1942), p. 4.

principle into legislation as a basis for a fundamental and enduring farm policy.[29]

In the fight for new general farm legislation in 1937, the A.F.B.F. found itself in the unusual position of alliance with the Administration against Congress. Generally speaking, the A.F.B.F. was likely to be closer to Congress than to the President. O'Neal himself, in a letter to a fellow Farm Bureau official, recognized this anomaly: "I find that we are in a most peculiar position. The President of the United States and his able Secretary Wallace, are wholeheartedly for us, but Congress, and it seems up to now, the rest of the farm organizations are very cool to our propositions, and in many instances, actually are hostile. . . ."[30] To another A.F.B.F. official O'Neal wrote in the same vein: "As I have been telling farmers, I am on the side of President Roosevelt who has shown by every word and act that he is for the farmers and with Secretary Wallace, and against the Democratic leadership in Congress."[31]

The trouble with Congress, according to O'Neal, was in the leadership of both the House and Senate committees on agriculture. While O'Neal praised Marvin Jones, chairman of the House committee, as one who had done much for agriculture, he deplored the fact that Jones was "opposed to drastic control measures" such as the A.F.B.F. was then seeking.[32] The chairman of the Senate committee was E. D. Smith of South Carolina, whose various proposals for special legislation for cotton had been frequently fought by the A.F.B.F. For its part, the A.F.B.F. wanted legislation which would treat all the basic commodities alike.

The mistake that the A.F.B.F. had made with Congress, in O'Neal's opinion, was in not having heeded his advice on the necessity of gaining control of these two committees. "Way back yonder," he complained, "when I begged for pressure on individual committee members by our state leaders, we could easily have passed the bill through the House."[33] He pointed out that the agriculture committees, above any of the other regular committees, dominated Congress' policies affecting farmers, and that it was "very difficult indeed to overcome the regular set-up and pass a bill without the approval of the Agricultural Committees."[34] This

---

[29] In 1937 Wallace gave a succinct definition of what he meant by the "ever-normal granary" in *The Agricultural Situation*, March, 1937, p. 9.

[30] O'Neal to Clifton Kirkpatrick, June 1, 1937.

[31] O'Neal to J. F. Porter, August 25, 1937.

[32] *Ibid.*

[33] *Ibid.*

[34] *Ibid.*

had been done to a large degree, however, in the cases of the three acts which had been the most stringent farm production control measures under the New Deal, namely, the Bankhead Act for controlling cotton, the Kerr-Smith Act for controlling tobacco, and the Warren Potato Act.[35]

The Agricultural Adjustment Act of 1938 as finally passed was a compromise between the Senate bill (the Pope-McGill bill, which was sponsored by the Farm Bureau) and the House bill, which the Farm Bureau had opposed as being "all but worthless for controlling surpluses or stabilizing prices."[36] The far stronger influence of the A.F.B.F. in the Senate than in the House of Representatives, a phenomenon which would become increasingly evident, is apparent here. The compromise by which the act of 1938 was agreed upon was worked out in a conference committee made up of representatives of the agricultural committees of both houses.[37]

The compromise was not acceptable to the National Grange, which opposed the bill because the Grange viewed "with deep disapproval" the compulsory character of production control which was one of the main features of the bill.[38]

While the Farm Bureau did not claim the paternity of the Agricultural Adjustment Act of 1938, as it had that of the 1933 act, the A.F.B.F. played a major role in the negotiations by which the 1938 act was written, and A.F.B.F. leaders supported the compromise.[39]

---

[35] *Ibid.* These acts virtually taxed nonco-operators out of production.

[36] *A.F.B.F. Official News Letter*, January 4, 1938.

[37] The Agricultural Adjustment Act of 1938 made provision for carrying on most of the procedures which had been used since 1933. But two which had been previously used only for special crops or in special emergencies now became general and normal practices. These were marketing quotas (as distinguished from acreage allotments), and price-support loans. The act of 1938 tied together the concepts which became the heart of the farm program, at least in the view of the Farm Bureau. These were production control, price-support loans, and parity prices. Nonrecourse loans on cotton and wheat were to be available at not less than 52 per cent and not more than 75 per cent of parity to those growers who co-operated—that is, to those who did not exceed their quotas or allotments. (The scheme for corn was somewhat more complicated.) Decision as to the exact level of the loan, within the range specified, was left to the discretion of the Secretary of Agriculture. In addition, the Secretary of Agriculture was authorized to continue to make "parity payments"— that is, direct payments to farmers to make up the difference between market prices and parity prices. The amount of such payments, however, depended upon the money made available by Congressional appropriation.

[38] The Grange to the members of the Senate, February 9, 1938, *Congressional Record*, February 11, 1938.

[39] A.F.B.F. executive committee to the members of the Senate, February 9, 1938, *A.F.B.F. Official News Letter*, February 16, 1938.

O'Neal's candid account of the procedure and the bill is given in a letter to a state Farm Bureau leader: "Senators Bankhead, Pope, McGill, Hatch and Arthur Capper have been exceedingly fine in asking us to advise with them daily. Of course they had to compromise with the House Conferees. . . . The whole procedure seemed to be compromise with the House Conferees and each time this was done, it weakened our original bill, but this was the best we could do under the circumstances."[40] It is noteworthy that O'Neal took for granted the necessity of compromise.

To Senator Pope, who had been one of the senatorial sponsors of the original Farm Bureau bill for a national farm program in 1937-38, O'Neal wrote: "You saved all of your bill that it was humanly possible to save, but it was entirely re-written in conference. Some of the best features were deleted, but the resulting bill was at least a start in the right direction. You saved the parity concept, but no method of raising money for parity payments for farmers was provided."[41]

That the parity concept had been saved in the act of 1938 was a source of deep satisfaction to the Farm Bureau, for by now "parity" was a sacred Farm Bureau slogan. That no method for raising money for parity payments to farmers was provided became a source of hazard to those Farm Bureau leaders who consequently had to press Congress for yearly appropriations.

In 1938 O'Neal was satisfied that the interests of both corn and cotton, the two major crops influencing Farm Bureau policy, would be benefited by the act of 1938, and that the sectional unity of Midwest and South within the Farm Bureau would be thus preserved. For corn farmers he predicted that price stability at near-parity levels would be achieved chiefly through commodity loans, since there was no considerable volume of export trade to affect the price otherwise. For cotton, tobacco, and rice farmers, who generally were favorable to rigid production control measures, he expected marketing quotas to play a major part in stabilizing supplies and prices. (The producers of these crops were considered much more likely to vote favorably on the imposition of quotas than were the Midwestern corn growers.) Wheat he rather brushed off by saying that loans should do as much for wheat farmers as for corn farmers.[42]

---

[40] O'Neal to R. M. Stiles, President of the United Georgia Farmers, the state unit of the Farm Bureau, January 26, 1938.

[41] O'Neal to James P. Pope, April 28, 1938.

[42] *A.F.B.F. Official News Letter*, February 16, 1938.

In addition to strengthening the devices of production control and commodity loans, a significant new means to guarantee a substantial percentage of "parity price" to farmers was made in the act of 1938. This was the device of "parity payments."[43] The act of 1938 authorized direct federal payments to producers of "the basic crops"—corn, wheat, cotton, rice, and tobacco—in addition to whatever other benefit payments they were receiving, for the purpose of bringing the total of market price plus payments received up near the parity level.

In the struggles which ensued to get Congress to make appropriations for the parity payments which had been merely authorized in the act of 1938, the Farm Bureau found an indispensable ally in urban labor. The basis for the alliance of these two groups was their common opposition to the "economy bloc" in Congress. The Farm Bureau needed non-farm support in Congress to obtain appropriations for "parity payments"; urban labor needed non-labor support to get appropriations for "works relief." It is significant that, after a hot fight, the appropriation in 1938 of $212,000,000 for parity payments to farmers was adopted on the final day of the Seventy-fifth Congress as an amendment to the Works Relief Act. That this friendship of farmers and laborers was a matter of horse-trading is evident.

A more refined way of expressing the relationship between farmers and urban labor was that of "reciprocity." This relationship was acknowledged by urban as well as by farm representatives. In 1938 Congressman John O'Connor of New York recounted various occasions on which the support of big city representatives in Congress, especially those from New York, had been decisive in the passage of farm bills, and he freely acknowledged that "at those times we had certain assurances of reciprocity."[44] For instance, he said:

I remember just at the close of the first session of this Congress, when a cotton bill was under consideration and it became necessary to change

[43] Actually this too was similar to a practice which had been used sporadically before. For example, in 1937 Congress appropriated $130,000,000 of Section 32 funds for "price adjustment payments" to cotton farmers who cooperated in the 1938 agricultural conservation program. The cotton price adjustment payments, however, constituted a special privilege to one crop, a principle which the A.F.B.F. opposed in favor of treating all the basic crops alike, as was done under the system of parity payments established in 1938.

[44] Quoted from a speech made in the House of Representatives, February 8, 1938, by Representative John O'Connor, *A.F.B.F. Official News Letter*, February 16, 1938.

enough votes to pass the bill. We got enough changes from New York and the surrounding territory to pass the bill. The McNary-Haugen bill was passed by votes from New York, just a handful. The Bankhead cotton bill was passed by just a few votes from New York. Of course, at those times we had certain assurances of reciprocity. For instance, at the time of the closing days of the first session of this Congress when some of us stood at this door to the Speaker's lobby and got the votes necessary to pass the cotton bill, we had pretty definite assurances that we would get considerable help from a certain section of this country on the wage-and-hour bill. History records the result of that hard and fast agreement. . . .[45]

The Wages and Hours bill of 1938 was under consideration at the same time as the parity payments appropriations. The A.F.B.F. contented itself with insisting, successfully, that agricultural labor be exempted from the provisions of the Wages and Hours Act.

The most dramatic instance of urban labor support for agricultural legislation occurred in 1939, when it was necessary for Congress to make another annual appropriation for parity payments, if such payments were to be available in the following year. The Farm Bureau was finding it very difficult indeed to overcome the resistance of the "economy bloc" in the House of Representatives to what the Farm Bureau considered reasonable appropriations. This "economy bloc," according to a Farm Bureau official publication, was led by Representative Woodrum of Virginia.[46] In the spring of 1939 the House killed the proposed appropriation for parity payments by an adverse vote.[47] The Senate restored the fund, although at a somewhat lower level than the Farm Bureau advocated—that is, at $225,000,000 rather than $250,000,000.[48] A conference report approved the restoration of the fund at $255,000,000. Then on June 22, 1939, the House defeated the conference report by a standing vote of 119 to 112. A few minutes later a roll-call vote in the House was demanded.[49] O'Neal gave credit to Mayor La Guardia of New York City for the eleventh-hour victory won by the farm forces in this roll-call vote.

According to O'Neal's story, when he learned that the bill for parity payment appropriations probably would not go through the House, he telephoned or telegraphed La Guardia. La Guardia came down to Washington by plane. He and O'Neal went over to the House lobbies while the vote was going on. Since the vote takes

---

[45] *Ibid.*
[46] *A.F.B.F. Official News Letter,* May 23, 1939.
[47] *Ibid.,* April 11, 1939.
[48] *Ibid.,* May 23, 1939.
[49] *Ibid.,* July 4, 1939.

about 45 minutes, they had time to call out some of the congressmen from the floor of the House. O'Neal called out Clarence Cannon and Marvin Jones, who were leading the fight for the appropriation. La Guardia called out some of the city representatives. La
Guardia had to argue with Representative Marcantonio (American
Labor, New York), who wanted to hold out for a definite promise
from O'Neal for reciprocity on labor measures. La Guardia told
Marcantonio, "You ought not even to ask Ed that." He further
pointed out to him how the Farm Bureau had stood with them on
constructive labor measures. The city representatives went back
and voted for the bill, which passed only by reason of the fact that
ten representatives from the biggest cities changed their original
votes from nay to yea.[50]

Whether the details of this occasion were remembered by O'Neal
with entire accuracy or not, it is significant that after ten years he
recalled the incident with enthusiasm as one of the great and crucial victories of the Farm Bureau, and that he freely gave credit
to the city representatives for indispensable assistance.

Some confirmation of the main outlines of O'Neal's account is
found in other Farm Bureau sources and in newspaper accounts.
Unfortunately none is available from the other chief participant
himself, Mayor La Guardia.

The account in the A.F.B.F.'s *Official News Letter*, published
July 4, 1939, is substantially the same as that remembered by
O'Neal ten years later, except for a few details. It appears from the
Official News Letter that La Guardia did not come down to Washington in response to O'Neal's urgent request, but that he sent a
telegram endorsing the agricultural appropriation and then came to
Washington to testify on relief appropriations. This, however, was
at the propitious moment for the farm group. The *News Letter*
story does not tell directly of the historic meetings in the lobbies of
the House, but it does hint at them in a dignified way:

Day after sending the telegram, Mayor La Guardia was in Washington
to testify on relief appropriations. While there, he contacted several city
Congressmen and urged their support of the farm bill. The mayor assisted
President O'Neal and W. R. Ogg, A.F.B.F. research director, in calling
together a number of representatives from city and country districts for
a series of conferences.

Some of the city Congressmen wanted assurances that the farm bloc
would support the elimination of some of the restrictions on W.P.A.

---

[50] This account was told to the writer in a personal interview with O'Neal,
May 23-24, 1949.

appropriations, now being considered by Congress. However, farm leaders told them that they had no authority to give such assurances. Congressmen from rural districts cited their record of having supported reasonable relief appropriations consistently. President O'Neal advised the spokesman for the city group of the position taken by the American Farm Bureau Federation on work relief in its statement to the President and Congress last January and advised that this was still the Federation's position and that he would so state in his reply to Mayor La Guardia's telegram. But he explained that he could not take any position on the specific restrictions in the W.P.A. bill which the city group wanted removed.[51]

W. R. Ogg, who the *News Letter* says was present at these conferences, independently asserted that they took place in the lobby of the House, with O'Neal and La Guardia calling representatives off the floor.[52] While O'Neal and Ogg were both Farm Bureau men, it seems probable that the memory of one would be a good check against the memory of the other, and unlikely that they would deliberately seek to mislead on such a point.

Richard Wilson, *Des Moines Register* correspondent, and Turner Catledge, writing in the *New York Times,* also state that approval for the parity payments appropriation was won with Mayor La Guardia's help, as a result of an understanding between the farm forces and urban representatives over agricultural appropriations and works relief appropriations.[53] Since the accounts of these two writers are quoted at length in the *A.F.B.F. Official News Letter,* it is reasonable to assume that the A.F.B.F. endorsed the accuracy of this interpretation. Wilson states categorically: "A victory on parity payments was brought about only by a deal between representatives of farm organizations and congressmen from New York and Chicago." The removal of the opposition of Marcantonio was the critical factor, according to Wilson. In explanation of the "deal," Wilson further states: "The original price for support of the parity payments provision was farm aid in taking off the $50,000 limit on W.P.A. construction projects voted by the house last week."[54]

In the O'Neal files are carbon copies of letters written by O'Neal on June 23, 1939, the day after the victory was won, thanking a number of the urban congressmen and senators. Among these were the city congressmen, Vito Marcantonio, Arthur D. Healy, John W. McCormack, and Joseph A. Gavagan. Also in the O'Neal files is a typewritten analysis of the record on the "House Vote on Agricul-

[51] *A.F.B.F. Official News Letter,* July 4, 1939.
[52] Ogg, personal interview, April 12, 1949.
[53] Reprinted in *A.F.B.F. Official News Letter,* July 4, 1939.
[54] *Ibid.*

tural Appropriations Bill, June 22, 1939." Attached to this is a memorandum on the Cannon Amendment (containing the parity payments appropriation). This memorandum makes clear that the decisive support came from ten congressmen from New York City, Chicago, and Boston.[55]

Congressman Tarver, speaking for representatives of farming areas, put the problem succinctly: "Now, the main difficulty we are met with in endeavoring to work out any sort of farm program is where to get the money. The farm Representatives in Congress represent only 30 per cent of the population, and we have to secure assistance from Members of Congress who represent urban communities before we are able to enact anything."[56]

The struggle for parity payments in 1939 is significant not only from the standpoint of Farm Bureau–labor relations, but also as a decisive turning point in the Farm Bureau's views on the financing of the national farm program.

This situation is summed up by O'Neal in a letter written August 30, 1939, shortly after the touch-and-go struggle for appropriations for parity payments: "There is no question that the Senate is overwhelmingly for farmers, but, as you say, the House showed up beyond question that it is going to be more and more difficult. . . . We must arrive at some more permanent plan for financing our agricultural program. . . ."[57]

The processing tax under the first A.A.A. had been one way of getting the money, but that way had been declared unconstitutional by the Supreme Court. Although the A.F.B.F. leaders believed that the processing tax itself had not been declared unconstitutional,[58] but only the way it had been used, Farm Bureau leaders had no intention of seeking to reintroduce this device for raising revenue. Under the first A.A.A., Midwestern farmers had come to be bitterly opposed to the processing tax, believing that the incidence of it in the case of hog producers fell on the farmers themselves.[59] In the

[55] "Memorandum on Cannon Amendment: 2nd Time," A.F.B.F., O'Neal Papers.

[56] U.S. House of Representatives, Subcommittee of the Committee on Appropriations, *Hearings on Agriculture Department Appropriation Bill for 1942. Part 2*, 77th Cong., 1st Sess., 1941, p. 432.

[57] O'Neal to Senator Clyde M. Reed, August 30, 1939.

[58] Chester Gray to O'Neal, October 26, 1937.

[59] This opinion is confirmed in the U.S. Department of Agriculture publication, *Agricultural Adjustment Programs, 1933-41*, p. 4. According to this study, the incidence of the processing tax usually was on the consumer, but in the case of hogs, prices were lowered by almost the full amount of the processing tax.

interest of Midwestern-Southern farm unity it was imperative therefore that the Farm Bureau support some other method of financing the farm program. O'Neal's letters reveal his groping among several alternatives, the one which he favored most being a manufacturers' sales tax which would be applicable to all manufacturers instead of solely to the processors of agricultural commodities. How to prevent certain Southern "cotton politicians" from insisting on the processing tax and thus producing commodity conflicts within agriculture was one of the major problems with which O'Neal had to deal. Concerning it, he wrote to Chester Davis:

> The Midwest area, particularly the cornbelt, feels that a manufacturer's sales tax is the proper way to raise revenue for parity payments and other necessary payments for the agricultural program, for they feel that a processing tax would not be practical for the cornbelt on cattle and hogs and so on, and if there was a processing tax on cotton and one on wheat, or if there was a certificate plan on both of these, that it would destroy the unity in agriculture that is so necessary to have.
>
> You recall in the last session of Congress what a terrible time we had in the House and in the Senate when the cotton boys were driving for large appropriations on cotton. We just had to get our heads together and organize a block in the Senate with representatives of corn, wheat, dairy, cotton, and hogs. In other words, in order to have unity between the corn, wheat, and cotton belts, there must be no processing tax. We are just driven to get the money some other way.[60]

It had been freely predicted that Congress could not be persuaded in 1939 to make appropriations for parity payments at all, and victory was won only after a most nerve-wracking period of uncertainty. Henceforth, during O'Neal's presidency, the A.F.B.F. redoubled its efforts to remove the farm program from dependence on the uncertainties and hazards of yearly appropriations by Congress from the treasury. After 1939, what the Farm Bureau increasingly emphasized for achievement of the goal of parity was "fair" (but not free) prices, supported by the government by means of various devices.[61] At the same time, organized labor was intensifying its efforts to do very much the same sort of thing by pushing for wages and hours legislation, under which a "fair" minimum price for labor would be guaranteed. But whereas the struggle of farm and labor groups for appropriations in Congress had brought

[60] O'Neal to Davis, November 18, 1939.

[61] Price-support schemes require some appropriations, of course, but not nearly so great an amount as direct payments to farmers. See George K. Brinegar, "Direct Payments to Producers," a statement in U.S. Congress, Joint Economic Committee, *Policy for Commercial Agriculture*, 85th Cong., 1st Sess. (November 22, 1957), p. 644.

them together against their common enemy, the "economy bloc," the pursuit by each group of higher compensation in the market place increasingly drove them apart. The year 1939 represents therefore not only a peak in cordiality between the Farm Bureau and urban labor, but a turning point in that relationship.

CHAPTER VIII

How Commodity Conflicts
Were Compromised

Achieving agricultural unity was almost a religion with Edward A. O'Neal, and his success in that direction is probably the outstanding accomplishment of his administration. To O'Neal there was nothing inconsistent in combining a national program for agriculture with deep local loyalties and regional interests. Statements such as the following indicate his appreciation of the fact that democracy demands compromise:

> One of the things I have learned in nearly 20 years of Farm Bureau work is that in this country you win with a majority. That's democracy. If the farm people of the South will stop to think that all the Southern votes in Congress can be offset by the votes of four leading industrial states in the North, they will begin to realize their helplessness in trying to fight their farm battles alone. Farmers have simply got to work together, in North, South, East and West to solve the national problem of agriculture, if they are to get what they want in their own regions.[1]

The four industrial states that O'Neal had in mind were: New York, with 45 votes; Pennsylvania, with 34; Ohio, with 24; and Michigan, with 17. The total, 120 votes, of these four industrial states exceeded the combined vote of all twelve cotton states, which was only 111.[2]

Earl Smith was even more specific in his statement of the necessity for compromise between farmers of the two great agricultural sections of the country, the Midwest and the South. A speech which

---

[1] "Minutes of the Southern Farm Bureau Training School, Memphis, Tennessee, August 24-26, 1939," A.F.B.F. regional files, folder marked "R. W. Blackburn."

[2] These figures are taken from a typewritten card on which the vote by each of the four regions is also given. At the bottom is the citation "Agricultural Appropriation Bill (First) May 23, 1939." A.F.B.F., O'Neal Papers.

he made, entitled "No North, No South, in Agriculture," was summarized in the official record:

> Mr. Smith spoke eloquently of the wiping out of sectional lines in the long fight for farm equality. He showed that the South and the Midwest together have 84.3 per cent of the total population and 83.4 per cent of the farms, which comprise 72.6 per cent of the farm acreage. The two regions have 75.2 per cent of the value of farm land and buildings in the nation, and receive 73.1 per cent of the farm income. The two regions are easily the dominant areas in American agriculture, and therefore they have a community of interest that demands close co-operation between the two regions.[3]

The A.F.B.F. was based upon sectional representation, but sectional representation was often, in fact, commodity representation. The Midwest's representatives, for example, were understood to be the spokesmen for corn, hogs, and soybeans; Southerners in general spoke for cotton and peanuts, while the North Carolina and Kentucky delegates in particular made sure that tobacco was "looked after," and Arkansas looked after rice. Wheat was represented by Kansas, Texas, and other states of the Great Plains. Wheat was not so strongly represented as corn, however, for the Farmers' Union was strong in the wheat belt. The Farm Bureau's constant wooing of the cattle raisers of the Great Plains was largely without success. The Northeastern states' representatives in the A.F.B.F. spoke for dairying, but dairying was also well represented in several other big farm organizations (the Grange and the National Milk Producers' Federation). Farm Bureau leaders of the far West spoke for fruit, wheat, and specialty crops, but most of these had strong commodity organizations as well. If keeping unity in American agriculture, as the Farm Bureau saw it, was basically a matter of keeping unity between corn and cotton, the other crops could not be ignored, and besides they sometimes provided room for essential maneuvering both within the Farm Bureau and in the Congress of the United States. For instance, Senator Alben Barkley of Kentucky was a key figure in achieving legislation affecting tobacco, and the mutual interest which he and the Farm Bureau had in tobacco legislation led to a mutually helpful, though perfectly proper, relationship on the general farm program.

Keeping unity within American agriculture necessitated, to O'Neal's and Smith's way of thinking, that all the main commodities should be treated alike. Any special favors to particular commodity

---

[3] "Minutes of the Southern Farm Bureau Training School, Memphis, Tennessee, August 24-26, 1939."

groups or sections, or even any differences in treatment which might be interpreted as special privileges, were sure to cause factional fights within agriculture. Hence the popularity of formulae.

The first A.A.A., with which the A.F.B.F. was so pleased, did apply the principle of "treating them all alike," if "them" is understood to be the so-called basic commodities—cotton, corn, wheat, and tobacco.[4] The use of a formula, in this instance the parity formula, was designed to give not only equality between agriculture and other industries, but equality of treatment among farm commodities. Even when events forced the recognition that no single formula could bring equivalent benefits to the producers of all the basic commodities, the A.F.B.F. was still loath to give up the formula principle. Only a common formula seemed to offer the impersonality and impartiality which the A.F.B.F. deemed essential to "keeping agricultural unity." O'Neal was always jittery about abandoning one formula for another, the reason being, as he described it, fear of "log rolling by commodity groups."[5] As he saw it, eventually the trouble came to be that "everybody has a formula."[6]

Among the actual or potential conflicts between commodities that the Farm Bureau had constantly to bear in mind in framing farm policy were: wheat as an alternative to corn for livestock feed; cottonseed meal or peanuts as an alternative to soybeans for high protein concentrates; butter as an alternative to margarine made from cottonseed oil, soybeans, or animal fats; livestock feeds as against the poultry and dairy products into which they are converted.

Fortunately, cotton and corn in their main uses are not competitive. Doubtless this fact was conducive to the alliance of the Midwestern and Southern farmers which in turn was the basis of the power of the Farm Bureau during the New Deal period.

It was not only within the Farm Bureau that O'Neal followed the principle that all the basic commodities should be treated alike. He used his wide acquaintance with leaders of other farm organizations to attempt to persuade them of the wisdom of following the same principle. A letter which he wrote to N. C. Williamson, Presi-

---

[4] There is of course no fixed group of "basic commodities." The A.A.A. of 1933 listed seven—corn, hogs, cotton, wheat, rice, milk, and tobacco. The list was varied from time to time, as for example by the addition of peanuts.

[5] O'Neal to John Strohn, associate editor of the *Prairie Farmer*, November 15, 1941.

[6] *Ibid.*

dent of the American Cotton Co-operative Association, is typical of the frequent attempts which O'Neal made in this area. After expressing appreciation for Williamson's co-operation in "the recent fight," O'Neal revealed that he was much disturbed over the position which the American Cotton Co-operative was now taking. He continued:

> If you followed the debate in Congress in the closing days of the session, you will note there was a great deal of heat shown by the majority of the Congressmen from the cornbelt, Democrats in particular, on the passage of the Byrnes resolution for adjustment payments to cotton farmers for the 1937 crop. They felt this was unfair to the rest of the basic crops. I hear since this action was taken that [it] has aroused a great deal of sectional feeling. It is going to be very difficult to keep this from developing further and hurting our chances for farm legislation. The Farm Bureau Board of Directors felt that similar treatment should be given to other basic agricultural commodities, which would help to smooth over this feeling. I am enclosing a copy of a resolution adopted on this . . . my hope is that you will continue to help hold together the Midwest and the South in fighting for a real farm bill. If this alliance should be broken, we will have no legislation.[7]

In his attempt to maintain unity between corn and cotton, O'Neal seems to have treated Earl Smith with kid gloves. Once he indicated extreme reluctance to go to see the President at Hyde Park unless Earl Smith were with him.[8] At another time, he conveyed to Henry A. Wallace the hostile reaction of Earl Smith to the certificate plan: "I talked to Earl very confidentially about what you and I were talking about. He is very much stirred up—that if you come out and talk about the certificate plan for cotton and wheat, you are going to split us wide open. They need the same treatment. . . . He is afraid of that scheme unless it would work for corn."[9]

As has been mentioned previously, Earl Smith was wont, at frequent intervals, to urge particular commodity groups to decide what they wanted by way of a farm program, and indicated that he would assist them to achieve their goals, on the understanding that they in turn would support the commodity policies in which he and the Midwestern group were interested. He likewise urged the board to forget about minor by-products such as the vegetable oils.

---

[7] O'Neal to Williamson, September 16, 1937.

[8] Telephone conversation between Secretary Wallace and O'Neal, September 16, 1936, A.F.B.F., O'Neal Papers (typescript). Smith was sick and could not go. O'Neal was willing to go with Wallace alone, but thought it was not safe to go with anyone else if Smith were not with him.

[9] Telephone conversation between Wallace and O'Neal, November 16, 1939, *ibid.*

In keeping with the gifted politicians which they were, O'Neal and Earl Smith tried always to widen areas of agreement. O'Neal was particularly adept at ignoring or glossing over matters on which there was likely to be conflict. Within the A.F.B.F., perhaps O'Neal's tendency not to bring conflict into the open did in fact lessen those conflicts, and promote the unity which he so fervently sought.

Earl Smith's motto was: "Support your friends and forget your enemies." In conformity with this strategy, the official publication of the Illinois Agricultural Association regularly rated the congressmen and senators from Illinois on the basis of their votes in Congress. But the rating scale was comprised only of the grades "excellent," "very good," "good," and "fair." There was no rating designated as "poor." Those who won either of the first two ratings were "entitled to support." Those rated "good" were "entitled to kindly consideration." Nothing was said about the rest.[10]

In dealing with Congress, the A.F.B.F. frequently worked with and through commodity blocs. For instance, in 1937 O'Neal wrote: "It was very evident in this extra session of Congress how effective the Cornbelt Bloc, which we organized, was in the lower house. We are not only going to try to strengthen this Bloc, but we must be able to organize a similar Bloc for the southern Congressmen."[11]

A glimpse of how the A.F.B.F.'s Washington representative worked with commodity blocs in Congress is afforded by a letter to O'Neal in 1940: "I have been waiting to hear from Howard Gray or Senator Bankhead as to whether the Senator is willing to organize the cotton belt Senators to go to see the President before contacting the Senators from the wheat belt. Unless the cotton belt Senators are willing to go ahead there would not be any use to try to organize a delegation from the wheat belt. My suggestion would be to get Norris and Capper to organize the wheat delegation if they are willing to do so."[12]

In attempting to preserve unity among the commodity interests both among farmers and in Congress, the A.F.B.F. was assisting the U.S. Department of Agriculture, so long as the Department of Agriculture and the A.F.B.F. were working toward a common farm pro-

---

[10] For an instance of this sort of rating, see *Illinois Agricultural Association Record*, November, 1940, pp. 4-5.

[11] O'Neal to Oscar Johnston of the National Cotton Council, December 21, 1937.

[12] W. R. Ogg to O'Neal, August 14, 1940. Howard Gray was President of the Farm Bureau of Alabama, Senator Bankhead's home state.

gram. This was one of the ways in which the A.F.B.F. gave the Department of Agriculture powerful political support. Some of Secretary Wallace's own efforts to hold the commodity interests together were recounted by him in 1939 when he told how he had been meeting with "the cotton Senators" for three days. He believed that the attitude of some of them, Bankhead in particular, was very good with regard to sectionalism. He further told O'Neal: "They realize their problem is such a one that they cannot get acceptance unless they have the co-operation of the corn and wheat folks. They want to team up with them to get more appropriations. . . . They agreed there had to be unity between wheat, cotton, and corn."[13]

Commodity conflicts were of two main sorts: intercommodity (e.g., between wheat and corn), and intracommodity (e.g., within cotton). Intercommodity conflicts actually seem to have been more amenable to compromise than those that were of an intracommodity nature.

Since the most troublesome of the intracommodity conflicts appear to have been those that plagued the cotton growers, the A.F.B.F.'s attempt to achieve a measure of cohesion in this area is of particular interest. Chief sources of this trouble seem to have been: (1) competition between the old and the new cotton areas; and (2) the number and variety of leaders and organizations, each attempting "to speak for cotton."

Competition between old and new cotton areas was exacerbated under the A.A.A. by the controls over production which provided cotton acreage allotments and eventually marketing quotas to states, counties, and individuals. These allotments were on a historical basis. Naturally, such a system favored the older cotton areas, which were chiefly east of the Mississippi. Without such protection, Southeastern farmers, other than those in exceptionally favorable circumstances, might have been gradually forced out of cotton production altogether. In the newer, largely irrigated cotton areas west of the Mississippi (such as those in Texas, New Mexico, Arizona, and California) the cost of producing cotton was being cheapened by mechanization on a scale more vast than was generally possible in the East. Given the American tradition of individual freedom, the course of events in cotton production probably would have conformed to one of the great themes in American history—namely,

[13] Telephone conversation between Wallace and O'Neal, February 2, 1939, A.F.B.F., O'Neal Papers (typescript).

the westward migration of crops. From the time when cheap wheat from the West forced New Englanders to turn to other farm products or to abandon their farms, this process had been going on, region after region. Now, under the New Deal legislation, while there was probably no conscious effort to arrest what had been one of the most dynamic forces in American history, there was inherent in the goal of stability of much of the early New Deal legislation for agriculture a negation of such forces.

Wrangling over what years should be designated as the historical period on which allotments should be computed was inevitable. The more recent the period, the more favorable it would be, of course, to the newer areas. One of the most difficult tasks which the A.F.B.F. attempted to perform was to bring about agreement as to how the national production quota should be alloted among the states. That compromises worked out within the A.F.B.F. were not always acceptable to groups of farmers concerned is illustrated by the formation of the Associated Irrigated Cotton Producers of New Mexico and Texas. The Washington representative of the A.F.B.F. reported that this new group was set up "to get a better base for lint cotton grown in irrigated areas than has been accorded that cotton in tripple [sic] A down to date."[14] He further reported that this group was virtually setting up an office of its own in Washington, and that it was not friendly to the Farm Bureau.[15]

Within the irrigated cotton areas, there was conflict over individual allotments between the established growers and new or potential growers which was similar to the conflict between the irrigated areas and the older areas over state allotments. While the individual allotments were made primarily on a historical basis, nevertheless, providing certain conditions were fulfilled, new growers were entitled to receive allotments. Since these allotments for new growers had to be provided out of the total state allotment, the established growers feared that their individual allotments would be cut. The situation was considered particularly dangerous to the established growers in areas where new irrigation projects were under construction.

For instance, the president of the New Mexico Farm Bureau wrote to O'Neal that in New Mexico, Arizona, and California they faced a real problem, in that there was a considerable amount of new land that could be brought into cultivation and a great amount

---

[14] Chester Gray to O'Neal, November 8, 1937.
[15] *Ibid.*

of old land upon which cotton had never been grown. If "fly by nights" were not shut out, the "real cotton growers," that is, the old established growers who were co-operators in the A.A.A., would find their allotments depleted. In New Mexico they believed that there should be a qualifying period of five years (instead of one year, as at that time) before new growers received an allotment, and that penalties for overplanting should be increased above the existing 3 per cent penalty.[16]

The internal conflicts among cotton producers might have been much more easily reconciled had there not been so many groups and persons attempting to act as spokesmen for that commodity. The Farm Bureau found it difficult to achieve unity on a program for cotton when several cotton commodity organizations as well as a number of individual Southern senators and congressmen each had separate and often conflicting programs for cotton. The individualism of the cotton South, as compared with the corn belt, was pointed out by O'Neal in a letter to Oscar Johnston: "Like you, I am so anxious that we get the cotton farmers *cotton organization conscious* so we can act effectively together. There are too many ideas and too many leaders in the South, therefore we have never gotten anywhere.... Our southern situation is a tragedy as far as the Congress is concerned, particularly the lower house. The Senators are more of one mind and are not so difficult to organize."[17] Later O'Neal found that Oscar Johnston and his Cotton Council increased the trouble which the Farm Bureau had with "too many ideas and too many leaders in the South."

The chief commodity organizations for cotton in the South were the American Cotton Co-operative Association, established as part of an earlier movement for co-operative marketing; and the Cotton Council, which was just being organized by Oscar Johnston in 1937. Neither of these organizations was associated with the Farm Bureau, although O'Neal in the beginning had hopes that the Cotton Council would work closely with the Farm Bureau.

The American Cotton Co-operative Association was a member of the National Council of Farmer Co-operatives (the Co-op Council). Sometimes O'Neal was able to count upon the American Cotton Co-operative Association to use its influence with the Co-op Council in favor of policies which coincided with those of the Farm Bureau, for instance on the reciprocal trade program.

---

[16] G. D. Hatfield to O'Neal, April 23, 1941.

[17] O'Neal to Johnston, December 21, 1937.

On the cotton program, however, in 1937 the president of the American Cotton Co-operative Association, N. C. Williamson, was opposing policies which O'Neal considered basic. Williamson informed O'Neal that he was "not disposed to appeal to the Co-op Council to support the general farm bill, because I think it will come to nought."[18] This bill was sponsored by the Farm Bureau, as is indicated by O'Neal's reference to it in letters to other Farm Bureau officials as "our bill."[19] Something of interorganizational rivalry is revealed in Williamson's statement that his people believed that they should work with Marvin Jones and his committee (the House Committee on Agriculture) in framing a bill that would be the committee's bill and not that of any one of the farm groups.[20] There were, additionally, basic policy differences. At this time O'Neal was working frantically to find a way to finance the farm program which would not require direct payments from the federal treasury. Williamson favored getting the Co-op Council to demand a direct payment from the treasury to cotton growers as compensation for the tariff they paid in the cost of things they bought. He believed that he had the support of Senator Smith of South Carolina in advocating such a program. Moreover, Williamson believed that no drastic measures to control production would be necessary.[21] To O'Neal, production control was fundamental to the success of the New Deal farm program. In this policy he believed that he had the support of Senator Bankhead of Alabama. O'Neal was particularly disturbed by Williamson's opposition to production control, and by Marvin Jones's apparent unwillingness to have a bill providing for effective production control. Further, O'Neal feared that the friendly Midwestern representatives would be so alienated by the demands for special subsidies to cotton that a national farm program would become an impossibility.[22]

Oscar Johnston's National Cotton Council was at first welcomed by O'Neal, though not without misgivings. The Cotton Council, as Johnston explained, was composed of "representatives of the six Raw Cotton Interests, namely, Producers, Ginners, Warehousemen, Merchants, Spinners, and Cottonseed Crushers."[23] The purpose of

---

[18] Williamson to O'Neal, June 19, 1937.

[19] O'Neal to J. F. Porter, September 24, 1937.

[20] Williamson to O'Neal, September 4, 1937.

[21] *Ibid.*

[22] O'Neal to Porter, September 24, 1937; O'Neal to Williamson, September 16, 1937.

[23] Johnston to O'Neal, January 26, 1941.

the Council was "to promote and expand the consumption of American-grown cotton, cottonseed, and the products thereof."[24]

Before he initiated his plan, Johnston went to the A.F.B.F. headquarters in Chicago, and spent half a day with O'Neal, Earl Smith, and Kirkpatrick (the Farm Bureau counsel), discussing the matter.[25] O'Neal was convinced that Johnston wanted to work with the Farm Bureau. "He promises me definitely," said O'Neal, "that he wants to work with the Farm Bureau, both state and national, and have no duplication of effort. . . . He does want to get a strong, militant Farm Bureau organization in the South to work with the cornbelt, in the American Farm Bureau family."[26] At Johnston's request, O'Neal gave him the names of several Farm Bureau leaders who could suggest people to represent the producers on the proposed Cotton Council.[27]

Nonetheless, O'Neal acknowledged that he had felt a good deal of trepidation about Johnston's proposed council. Unless the council were dominated by producers (i.e., farmers) O'Neal foresaw trouble. Consequently he felt that he could hardly refuse to help Johnston get "real representatives of producers."[28] In order to ensure that the Cotton Council would be controlled by producers rather than processors or merchants, O'Neal believed that it would be necessary for the Farm Bureau "to keep its hand on the throttle" through the Southern state farm bureau organizations.[29] He believed that the Southern state farm bureau leaders could keep Johnston in line.[30]

The Washington representative of the A.F.B.F. was even more dubious about the Cotton Council. He had been informed that the Cotton Council planned to engage in legislative activities in Washington for the cotton South. He believed that, with the Southern commissioners of agriculture already in Washington as a lobby for the South, if the South set up another special lobby for its regional interests, this "might be just too much from the points of view of the other regions."[31]

---

[24] *Ibid.*
[25] O'Neal to Chester Gray, November 2, 1937.
[26] *Ibid.*
[27] O'Neal to G. F. Holsinger, President of the Virginia Farm Bureau, June 29, 1938.
[28] *Ibid.*
[29] *Ibid.*
[30] O'Neal to Chester Gray, November 2, 1937.
[31] Gray to O'Neal, October 28, 1937.

Farm Bureau misgivings about the Cotton Council were well founded, for by 1939 O'Neal was talking about the trouble the Farm Bureau was having with Oscar Johnston's influence in the South. Apparently the Mississippi Farm Bureau had fallen under his influence, but the leaders of the Alabama Farm Bureau set out to combat it. By 1941 a Southern organizer of the Farm Bureau spoke of the cotton program of the Cotton Council as being "diametrically in contradiction to our farm bureau program." He wrote O'Neal of the struggle he had gone through in Texas, with "an enemy" who spent twelve hours trying to get Walter Hammond, President of the Texas Farm Bureau, to accept the cotton program of the Cotton Council.[32]

The basic difference between the program of the Cotton Council and that of the Farm Bureau seems to have been on the question of how parity prices to farmers could best be achieved. The Farm Bureau insisted that farmers should get parity prices in the market place (through a price-support program), thus obviating the necessity for annual appropriations from Congress. In order to ensure that support prices should be close to parity, the Farm Bureau was pressing strenuously in 1941 for mandatory commodity loans at 85 per cent of parity. The Cotton Council's program was the direct antithesis. It opposed high commodity loans, and favored direct payments by the government to farmers. Under such a scheme, the market price of cotton might be low, but the difference between the market price and parity would be made up by direct payments. Since the Cotton Council had been organized "to carry on the necessary advertising and publicity campaigns to expand consumption of cotton,"[33] it was logical that the Cotton Council would favor some scheme for compensating farmers other than one involving a higher market price. Such higher prices for raw cotton probably would encourage increased use of competing fibers, which was exactly what the Cotton Council was organized to combat.

The Farm Bureau leaders suspected, however, that the Cotton Council's opposition to government measures for raising farm prices was due to dominance of the council by processors rather than producers. A low market price for raw cotton would, of course, be favorable to cotton processors and merchants.

---

[32] This letter was written to O'Neal, March 1, 1941.

[33] Oscar Johnston to Walter Randolph, January 7, 1941 (carbon copy), enclosed in a letter from Johnston to O'Neal, January 7, 1941.

Eventually it was Walter Randolph, President of the Alabama Farm Bureau, who took the lead for the A.F.B.F. in its attempts to insist that the "producer call the tune" on the Cotton Council, but this was apparently not fully successful until 1945.[34]

In addition to differences on policy, there soon developed inter-organizational rivalry between the A.F.B.F. and the National Cotton Council. Apparently Farm Bureau officials had been reassured at first by what they believed was a promise on the part of the National Cotton Council not to engage in national legislative activities. Evidence that this alleged promise was being broken was presented by the Washington representative of the A.F.B.F. to O'Neal in 1939: "I enclose a copy of a publication issued by the National Cotton Council on June 16, 1939 in which you will note they have mentioned cotton legislation as the first major objective in their program. Since this is their own official publication, it is concrete evidence that they have violated their understanding with our state Farm Bureau leaders not to engage in national legislative activities."[35] O'Neal himself believed that the function of the Cotton Council was to promote the use of cotton. When Oscar Johnston consulted him before setting up the council, O'Neal frankly advised him against getting into the legislative field. In 1941, while expressing his admiration of "Oscar" and deploring the differences between the Farm Bureau and the Cotton Council, O'Neal again bluntly "advised" the Cotton Council to leave legislative activities to the Farm Bureau. In a letter to the executive secretary of the National Cotton Council, he wrote: "I don't think under any sense you should get into the legislative field. Let the southern Farm Bureaus, representing the southern cotton producers, handle this end of the business."[36]

The legislative activity of the Cotton Council was cited by the Washington representative of the A.F.B.F. as an outstanding example of a trend in recent years for commodity groups to set up their own legislative representation in Washington. He suggested to O'Neal that the best way to overcome this trend was for the Farm Bureau to provide an expanded service to deal with commodity and regional problems as well as national problems.[37] One

---

[34] *Cotton Trade Journal*, January 27, 1945, p. 2.

[35] W. R. Ogg to O'Neal, October 16, 1939.

[36] O'Neal to William Rhea Blake, October 16, 1941.

[37] W. R. Ogg, "Memorandum for President O'Neal, December, 1939," A.F.B.F., O'Neal Papers.

way to stop a rival organization was to take over its functions.

Not only did the Farm Bureau have to contend with conflicting policies for cotton sponsored by other organizations, but with individual Southern leaders. Chief among these was Senator "Cotton Ed" Smith of South Carolina, who frequently sponsored special legislation for cotton. An illustration of the Farm Bureau's troubles with such Southern political leaders was described by O'Neal: "The situation here in regard to cotton is very chaotic at times but it begins to look now like things are shaping up our way. However, we have a difficult situation in the Senate. Several of the leading Senators from the cotton states have banded together in a little block. They are opposing the export plan advocated by us and the President."[38]

The intracommodity conflicts within cotton were, of course, never completely resolved. What O'Neal ardently wished and worked for was a strong Farm Bureau organization in the South which could unify the policies of cotton producers and thus enable them to make effective compromises with the farmers of the corn belt. This, he believed, was the only hope the South had for securing national legislation in its favor.

How the A.F.B.F. functioned in bringing about compromises in conflicts *between* commodities is illustrated in the process by which the A.F.B.F. agreed upon a resolution proposing mandatory commodity loans[39] on the basic crops at a rate of 85 per cent of parity. This resolution was adopted at the annual meeting of the A.F.B.F. in 1940, and it became the basis of the law enacted by Congress in 1941.

This resolution, and the law which was an outcome of it, represented the high point of sectional compromise between Midwestern and Southern farmers working through the A.F.B.F. That it was primarily a compromise of commodity conflicts rather than of sectional conflicts, however, is evinced by the fact that wheat was allied with cotton rather than with corn. Most important in bringing cotton and wheat together was the fact that these two crops were, in the main, marketed directly by farmers, whereas most corn was marketed indirectly by farmers in the form of hogs. By 1940, when

[38] O'Neal to Romeo Short, President of the Arkansas Farm Bureau, April 1, 1939.

[39] Thus, instead of allowing any discretion to the Secretary of Agriculture, the loans were made mandatory and the exact loan level was specified in the legislation,

cotton farmers were demanding a government program which would guarantee higher market prices, corn farmers were beginning to doubt that higher market prices for corn would be desirable, since such prices might disturb corn-hog relationships. The cotton and the wheat representatives within the A.F.B.F. were willing to accept production controls in order to secure the higher price levels. The corn belt representatives were beginning to believe that higher price levels were not so desirable as was freedom from restrictions on production.

Nevertheless it was essential that agreement between corn and cotton be reached within the A.F.B.F., for it was believed that both the power of the A.F.B.F. and the sectional alliance of Midwestern and Southern farmers depended upon it. The wheat interests were not so strongly represented within the A.F.B.F.

Key figures in the process by which the resolution was adopted and the law enacted appear to have been Walter Randolph and Earl Smith of the Farm Bureau, and John H. Bankhead (who like Randolph was from Alabama) of the U.S. Senate.

Bankhead was looked upon by the A.F.B.F. as its chief leader for cotton in the Senate. Senator Bankhead was not, however, controlled by the Farm Bureau. He was his own man, strong enough in his home state to be independent. While he did not hesitate to work with the Farm Bureau on their policies if he agreed with them, equally he did not hesitate to fight the Farm Bureau when he felt occasion demanded it—namely, over the Farm Security Administration. Walter Randolph, who claimed to be close to Senator Bankhead, was quoted as saying that if he could get to Senator Bankhead first, he was sure he could handle him, "but when once the Senator took a bull-dog stand on an issue, that all Hell could not change him."[40]

For some time prior to the annual meeting of the A.F.B.F. in 1940, Southern Farm Bureau leaders had been discussing the desirability of high support prices—in fact they had been calling for mandatory commodity loans at 100 per cent of parity. Randolph took the lead in this proposal. The gist of his account of its progress follows.

Action started at the annual meeting of the Alabama Farm Bureau in October, 1940, when a resolution calling for loans at 100 per cent of parity was adopted. In November Randolph went to

[40] R. G. Arnold to O'Neal, November 5, 1940.

Senator Bankhead's home in Alabama, and got him to agree to introduce a bill for this purpose in the Senate. At the annual convention of the A.F.B.F. in December, 1940, Randolph of Alabama and Ransom Aldrich of Mississippi were at first the only ones in favor of the policy. But they got Romeo Short of Arkansas, who was rather reluctant to come out for the policy, to agree that on the resolutions committee whatever any two of the three stood for they would all back. They thought that O'Neal was with them too, but of course he could not say so. In the resolutions committee it appeared at first that these three were the only ones out of some 30-odd members who favored the measure. Earl Smith of Illinois, who was chairman of the resolutions committee, was at first very much opposed, for like the other Midwestern delegates at that time he was opposed to high mandatory loans. But the Southerners kept talking. Finally, Earl Smith proposed a compromise at 85 per cent of parity, and this was adopted by the resolutions committee and by the annual convention.[41]

Earl Smith confirmed that the Southern delegates did propose setting the loan level at 100 per cent of parity, and that it was he who proposed 85 per cent as a compromise.[42]

Senator Bankhead, however, at first refused to accept the compromise agreed upon by the A.F.B.F. He was insistent upon 100 per cent of parity for cotton, though quite willing to put into his bill what the "corn fellows" wanted for corn if they would let him know. In explanation of his stand, he wrote:

> The compromise . . . was not acceptable to me and I advised representatives of the Farm Bureau that I would acquiesce in the 85 per cent loan for corn, but would insist upon 100 per cent loan for cotton. My bill was introduced in line with that statement. I further stated that I would be governed by the attitude of the representatives of the corn producers and the wheat producers in the Senate, and if the representatives of the corn producers wanted to increase corn to 100 per cent, or the representatives of the wheat producers wanted to decrease wheat down to 85 per cent, I would follow their wishes.[43]

To O'Neal he wrote: "I will, of course, make no change in the bill on the subject of corn without the approval of you and your group who represent so many corn producers."[44]

[41] Walter Randolph, personal interview, May 26-27, 1949.
[42] Earl Smith, personal interview, July 18, 1949.
[43] Bankhead to Congressman Fred C. Gilchrist, April 5, 1941 (carbon copy), enclosed in a letter from Bankhead to O'Neal, April 5, 1941.
[44] Bankhead to O'Neal, April 5, 1941.

Meanwhile, Walter Randolph of Alabama had pledged his loyalty to the compromise agreed upon by the A.F.B.F., and promised to continue to urge Senator Bankhead to sponsor the bill on commodity loans with a maximum of 85 per cent of parity for all five of the so-called basic commodities. Randolph believed that if everybody in the A.F.B.F. stayed together, they could get Bankhead's bill in line with their policy. Further, Randolph promised to testify in support of the national Farm Bureau's position.[45]

O'Neal was perturbed because Senator Bankhead's insistence on 100 per cent of parity for cotton went beyond the resolution of the A.F.B.F. He had reason for believing that it would divide corn and cotton. "Mr. Smith claims it will throw out the whole law," said O'Neal.[46] A member of the staff of the Washington office of the A.F.B.F. reported that they had been forced to compromise with Senator Bankhead, and were now practically rudderless because they were not adhering to the A.F.B.F. resolution.[47]

O'Neal was disturbed also by an article in the May 3 issue of *Wallace's Farmer* which maintained that only 27 per cent of Iowa farmers wanted a higher corn loan rate at all (i.e., above the 75 per cent rate then in effect). To O'Neal this was incredible. "I just don't believe it," he wrote to Francis Johnson, President of the Iowa Farm Bureau.[48] He was reassured by Johnson, who thought that the article and the survey on which it was based reflected the thinking of the author as much as of farmers.[49]

When the Bankhead Mandatory Loan Act was finally passed, it set the loan rate at 85 per cent of parity on *all five* of the basic commodities. Thus, in effect it established support prices at this level, and it followed the principle of treating all the basic commodities alike. It seems probable that the compromise agreed upon at the A.F.B.F. annual meeting of December, 1940, was responsible for determining the final form of the act. Thus one of the most serious of intercommodity conflicts was resolved by compromise, although only temporarily. Almost immediately further attempts were made to raise the loan level, and once again O'Neal found himself, as he phrased it, "in a jam."

[45] Telegram from Randolph to O'Neal, February 19, 1941.
[46] Telephone conversation between W. R. Ogg, H. F. Hall, Assistant Director of Research of the A.F.B.F., and O'Neal, February 18, 1941, A.F.B.F., O'Neal Papers (typescript).
[47] *Ibid.*
[48] O'Neal to Johnson, May 5, 1941.
[49] Johnson to O'Neal, May 6, 1941.

While Senator Bankhead did not acknowledge the influence of the A.F.B.F. in setting the level of the loan at 85 per cent of parity, he did pay tribute to the power of the A.F.B.F. in facilitating the passage of the law. Bankhead wrote:

Prior to this year the membership of the Bureau has not been large enough and the activities of the officers and members of the organization have not been equal to the occasion on account of superior forces resisting the passage of favorable farm legislation. This year, with an increased membership, all of the Farm Bureau organizations went into vigorous action in support of the 85 per cent of parity price loan bill which I introduced and handled. The helpful support of effective, far-flung, and greatly interested farmers' organizations and members contributed in the most powerful way to bring about favorable action by Congress on my bill. . . . The producers of the basic commodities for the first time since immediately following the World War will now receive parity price for these commodities. We have been struggling since 1932 to accomplish that objective. I feel that we have a new day in rural life ahead of us. I would like very much to see every farmer in Alabama become a member of the Farm Bureau Federation.[50]

This letter from Bankhead carried a rather dubious compliment, since it implied that the Farm Bureau was too weak before 1941 to have had much influence. Doubtless his thinking was conditioned by the fact that in his home environment, the South, the Farm Bureau was relatively weak in membership until about that time.

The act was a crucial one, for it established the principle of high support prices by means of mandatory commodity loans. Though originally based on a compromise, the principle of high support prices which it embodied led to conflict between the Farm Bureau forces and the forces of urban labor, and to a splintering of unity within the Farm Bureau organization itself.

The one major commodity which appears to have been most nearly free from both intercommodity and intracommodity conflicts was tobacco. This crop seems always to have enjoyed an especially favored position within the A.F.B.F. as well as in national legislation. For its favored position within the A.F.B.F., probably the chief explanation is revealed incidentally by O'Neal in the following memorandum regarding instructions given to the A.F.B.F.'s Washington representative, on the request by tobacco growers for special treatment: "Phoned Mr. Ogg in regard to Flannagan Bill to change parity base period [on tobacco]. See no objection to it as our tobacco growers are unanimously for it. Will not affect other

[50] Bankhead to Walter Randolph, June 12, 1941, Alabama Farm Bureau files, Montgomery.

commodities. Instructed Ogg to get behind it."[51] Thus the unity among tobacco growers, and the belief within the A.F.B.F. that the policies they desired would not hurt the producers of other farm commodities, account in part at least for the special privileges which tobacco was accorded in national legislation.

[51] Memorandum initialed "E. O. N.," August 26, 1940, A.F.B.F., O'Neal Papers.

CHAPTER IX

Reconciliation: The Reciprocal
Trade Program

The most deep-seated and apparently irreconcilable difference of all those which existed within the A.F.B.F. concerned the issue of foreign trade. Over this issue there was sectional conflict, with roots deep in history—Midwestern isolationism versus Southern internationalism. There was the most fundamental commodity conflict of all, growing out of the fact that the market for corn-hog producers was chiefly a domestic one, whereas cotton was traditionally sold on a world market. And accompanying these was the political schism between the Democrats, who favored a lowering of tariff barriers, and the Midwestern Republicans, to whom a vote against tariff protectionism would have seemed a repudiation of Abraham Lincoln and the Emancipation Proclamation.

In reconciling these forces, Edward A. O'Neal rose above the stature of an interest-group politician. Although his triumph was not complete, he revealed the qualities of responsible statesmanship which won him respect from those who differed from him on many issues. This was his supreme effort at mediation.

A study of the relationship of the Farm Bureau to the reciprocal trade program also reveals: (1) the gradual change of a Farm Bureau policy from one position to another; and (2) how the Farm Bureau continued to work in harmony with the Roosevelt administration in some areas of policy after a split had already occurred in others.

In the 1920's the A.F.B.F. favored a high tariff policy for agriculture. Perhaps this was a reflection of Midwestern dominance in the Farm Bureau. The A.F.B.F. point of view, however, was not based on defense of tariffs per se, but only on the argument that if other industries were to be protected by tariffs, then so should agriculture. Chief credit for the enactment of the emergency tariff of May 27, 1921, was claimed by the A.F.B.F. The annual report of 1921 states explicitly: "We feel that it is not too much to take the major portion of credit for this piece of legislation, that has meant so much to the wool grower, for the American Farm Bureau Federation."[1] Perhaps the acme of this sort of thinking was reached in the proposal in Illinois that a tariff be placed on bananas, in order to protect the fruit growers of Illinois.[2]

The A.F.B.F. also took part in the National Agricultural Conference called by President Harding in 1922, which recommended further upward revision of the tariff. Subsequently, the A.F.B.F. supported the increase in tariffs in the Fordney-McCumber Act of 1922. The explanation of this mistake, which O'Neal later offered, was: "We, along with everybody else at the time, failed to realize that the change of this country from a debtor status to that of a creditor called for a new foreign policy. We just didn't appreciate the significance of this change, and apparently some people don't appreciate it even now [in 1940]."[3]

Confidence in the usual sort of tariff for agriculture waned as domestic surpluses piled up. But the McNary-Haugen proposal, to which the Midwestern farmers gave their support so wholeheartedly in the middle and late 1920's, was no outgrowth of antitariff sentiment. Rather it was simply an attempt to give the American farmer a tariff equivalent which would be effective. The gist of the proposal was that an "American" price should be maintained for American farm products on the domestic market, and that there should be export dumping of the surpluses. In the words of George Peek, who is generally recognized as the chief originator of the plan, the goal was "to secure equality for agriculture in the benefits of the protective tariff."[4]

After the Republican Party, under the leadership of Herbert Hoover, had rejected McNary-Haugenism at its national convention in 1928, the Farm Bureau turned back to the ordinary tariff system, with some lingering hope that the solution to the farmer's difficulties might be found in making the rates higher and higher.

---

[1] A.F.B.F., *Annual Report,* 1921, p. 53.

[2] *Bureau Farmer* (Illinois ed.), April, 1928, pp. 19 ff.

[3] U.S. House of Representatives, Committee on Ways and Means, *Hearings on Extension of Reciprocal Trade Agreements Act. Part 2,* 76th Cong., 3d Sess. (January 20-26, 1940), pp. 1669-70.

[4] Peek and Johnson, *op. cit.,* p. 5.

142] *The Farm Bureau and the New Deal*

In 1929 an A.F.B.F. resolution endorsed the Hoover tariff program, called for higher tariffs on agricultural products, and advocated the granting of immediate independence to such dependencies as the Philippines, whose commodities were entering the United States market duty free.[5] Other resolutions through 1931 continued in this tenor.

According to O'Neal, it was the consequences of the Hawley-Smoot tariff of 1930 that at last opened the eyes of the great rank and file of farmers to the fact that higher tariffs were not a solution to the surplus problem in agriculture. Farmers found the protection given most agricultural prices in the Hawley-Smoot tariff a "mirage." In 1932 the tariff on wheat was 42 cents a bushel, but the price of wheat was 30 cents a bushel. Farmers were getting 10 to 20 cents a bushel on their corn, although the tariff on corn was 25 cents a bushel. Industrial tariffs, on the other hand, were more effective in keeping up prices of industrial products, and thus the disparity between agricultural and industrial prices increased. At last farmers "became convinced that every time they were lured into the tariff game they got traded out of their shirts."[6]

Though the Hawley-Smoot tariff of 1930 may have demonstrated the futility of trying to solve the farm surplus problem by such means, the A.F.B.F., which was still largely Midwestern in the composition of its membership, was by no means ready to take a leading role in support of the reciprocal trade program in the early 1930's.

The position of President O'Neal, a Southerner and a Democrat, was, however, a forthright one favoring return to freer trade. An incident that reveals his genuine and consistent belief in this principle occurred when a fellow Southerner, Donald Comer, President of the American Cotton Manufacturers' Association, tried to win his support for a tariff on burlap and jute bags. Comer's argument was: "We should save as much of our home market as possible for our cotton. . . . I think our southern farmer has a lot more to be gained by selling truck to nearby industry than continuing to export cotton except in such quantities as will bring a fair price."[7] Refusing to be sidetracked by pursuit of a minor advantage from what he considered to be the larger welfare of cotton, and in fact of all

---

[5] A.F.B.F., *Resolutions of the Annual Meeting*, 1929.
[6] U.S. House, *Hearings, Extension of Reciprocal Trade Agreements Act. Part 2*, pp. 1671-72.
[7] Comer to O'Neal, July 2, 1936.

farmers, O'Neal replied: "Of course, you know I have always been for protecting the cotton textile industry, but I am afraid I cannot go along with you on raising the tariffs higher and higher. I don't see how it is possible for the cotton producer to stand for nationalism. We certainly have to have an export outlet and we must not strike at our best customers with high tariffs."[8] This position was reiterated even more strongly by O'Neal when Dr. Duncan, President of the Alabama Polytechnic Institute, wrote to inquire if there was anything which they could do about Comer's proposal.[9] O'Neal's reply was: "Naturally one is sympathetic with Comer's point of view, but it would be disastrous for the southern farmers, and in fact all of our farmers, for us to go nationalistic."[10]

O'Neal's private position was not very important, however, unless he could win a majority of the board of directors of the A.F.B.F. to it, and they in turn must carry their respective states. The skill and finesse, yet dignity and honesty with which he accomplished this task reveal O'Neal at his best. Preferring always to accept the best compromise he could get rather than to bring conflict into the open, O'Neal worked patiently to further the agricultural unity to which he was so devoted, and in spite of troubled undercurrents, to bring the public policy of the A.F.B.F. around to an endorsement of the reciprocal trade program.

In 1933 the position taken by the A.F.B.F. on tariff policy was cautious and largely noncommittal. The resolution on tariffs adopted by the board of directors of the A.F.B.F. immediately following the Roosevelt inauguration states: "That we oppose any reciprocal trade agreements that do not adequately safeguard the interests of agriculture."[11] Negative as this statement was, it was the first step away from the traditional high tariff policy that had hitherto dominated the foreign trade program of the A.F.B.F.

A year later, in March, 1934, O'Neal brought up the question again. This time, by another cautious step, the A.F.B.F. came a bit closer toward support of the reciprocal trade program, but not much closer. In effect, the executive committee of the board of directors was empowered to support the Roosevelt administration's foreign trade program, "if and when the proper assurance is given by the Administration that the rightful interest of agriculture will

---

[8] O'Neal to Comer, July 7, 1936.
[9] L. N. Duncan to O'Neal, June 30, 1936.
[10] O'Neal to Duncan, July 6, 1936.
[11] A.F.B.F., *Minutes of the Board of Directors,* March 8-9, 1933.

be fully protected in the administration of such policy."[12] The emphasis was obviously on the qualifying clause. Still, to declare that "we will support, if" was less negative than the preceding year's statement, "we will oppose, unless."

It was not until 1935 that the A.F.B.F.'s board of directors adopted a policy which could be considered favorable to the reciprocal trade program. Apparently O'Neal felt that the time had come when he could press for it, for the minutes state: "He urged the importance of taking a positive position with a view to promoting such reciprocal trade agreements instead of keeping ourselves in a mere negative position of opposing specific items in proposed treaties that we do not like."[13]

It was at this time too that O'Neal proposed that a special study of the possibilities of reciprocal trade treaties should be made for the A.F.B.F. in order that its leaders and members might proceed on the basis of factual information.[14] On a less high but probably equally persuasive plane, he argued that advantageous agreements might be reached with foreign nations who would accept larger quantities of American farm surpluses in exchange for the acceptance by the United States of larger quantities of their industrial goods. The minutes report the bare fact: "Without objection the proposed policy with respect to the reciprocal trade treaties was approved by the Committee."[15]

The most powerful centers of opposition to the reciprocal trade program were the states of Illinois and California. O'Neal was particularly disturbed because the corn belt attempted through the device of excise taxes to achieve the same end as would have been achieved by raising the tariff. This maneuver exemplifies the sectional split which extended beyond the Farm Bureau to political parties as well. Earl Smith argued, along the same lines as George Peek, that it was illogical to be asking the American farmers to reduce production without at the same time protecting them from imported competitive farm products. Practically all of those foreign products which he mentioned particularly as requiring an excise tax were possible competitors with products of the corn belt—foreign fats and oils versus lard, foreign blackstrap molasses versus corn alco-

---

[12] *Ibid.*, March 1-2, 1934.

[13] A.F.B.F., "Minutes of the Executive Committee," *ibid.*, January 8-10, 1935.

[14] This proposal was carried out in 1939.

[15] A.F.B.F., "Minutes of the Executive Committee," *Minutes of the Board of Directors*, January 8-10, 1935.

hol, foreign tapioca versus cornstarch.[16] O'Neal fumed privately, but apparently was prevented by his Farm Bureau position from taking any action against such subterfuges. To his old friend J. F. Porter, President of the Tennessee Farm Bureau, to whom he frequently unburdened himself, he expressed his frustration:

The selfish high-tariff groups are attacking from all quarters through excise taxes. I guess you noted the one put on pork in the House the other day. This is of course a way of raising a tariff. I feel it is short-sighted, yet Democrats in the corn belt area supported this measure. It has put us in an embarrassing position—we can't oppose it. Other groups are going to try the same plan with beef, eggs, etc. Secretary Hull says, it makes it exceedingly difficult to get a trade agreement with Great Britain under such circumstances. Another very bad result, as I see it, is that it is driving a wedge betweeen the south and corn belt, as most of our southern congressmen voted against the excise tax. I, of course, have not come out against it, and can't as I see it. I am trying to carry out the policies of the Farm Bureau.[17]

It was the proposed reciprocal trade treaty with Argentina which particularly aroused the suspicion both of the corn belt and of California, to say nothing of the range livestock area. O'Neal himself warned the A.F.B.F. Washington representative to be very careful in analyzing this treaty, for, he said: "You know there is dynamite in a treaty of this kind in the minds of our farmers. . . ."[18] Apparently O'Neal felt compelled to follow the advice of Earl Smith to make concessions to the corn belt area because of their antagonism to this treaty. In a letter to the Washington representative, O'Neal said that he doubted the necessity of the Farm Bureau's having anything further to say on the Argentine trade agreement, but that Vice-President Smith thought "that it would be well for me to supplement the brief [already given] with a letter pointing out the dangers to our A.A.A. program in negotiating such a treaty, particularly in the Cornbelt area."[19]

The California Farm Bureau's position, publicly as well as privately, was one of outright opposition to the policy adopted by the A.F.B.F. in 1935 on the tariff. There was no subterfuge, no imputation of disloyalty—it was simply understood that the California state organization could not accept that particular policy of the

---

[16] Smith to Chester Thompson, a member of the Ways and Means Committee of the House of Representatives, April 8, 1936. The letter is a copy sent to O'Neal.

[17] O'Neal to Porter, March 23, 1938.

[18] O'Neal to W. R. Ogg, September 1, 1939.

[19] O'Neal to Ogg, October 11, 1939; see also O'Neal to Ogg, June 27, 1938.

A.F.B.F. which called for a return to freer trade. California's position vis-à-vis the A.F.B.F. on this issue was made possible by the
decentralized structure of the A.F.B.F. California was not, however,
a typical state farm bureau, being more autonomous than most.
California, like the corn belt, was particularly disturbed about the
proposed Argentine trade treaty. The Californians had understood
that the purpose of the reciprocal trade treaties was to reduce ex-
cessive industrial tariffs, but the proposed trade treaty with Argentina, they believed, opened up an entirely new philosophy. They
feared that it would set a precedent for treaties with Latin-Ameri-
can republics, which were chiefly producers of agricultural commodities, some of them competitive with crops produced in the
United States. In particular, they opposed the freer importation of
Argentine flax seed.[20]

When the proposal for trade agreements with Argentina and
Uruguay was abandoned, the A.F.B.F. interpreted this as strengthening the trade agreements program by increasing the chances for
Congressional approval of it (a specious bit of reasoning). Farmers
were reassured by the refusal of Secretary Hull to make concessions which might be injurious to agricultural products. The products in question were Argentine canned beef and linseed oil, upon
which the U.S. government wished to establish quotas to protect
domestic products. The Argentine government refused to agree to
such quotas. The State Department's action was in accord with a
recommendation made by the A.F.B.F. at its annual meeting.[21]

The conflict within the A.F.B.F. over tariff policies was by no
means simply one of Midwestern and Western opposition to a
Southern free trade policy. The issue of raising the tariff on jute
illustrates the complexity of agricultural tariff policy. In the case of
jute, the call for a higher tariff came from the cotton belt, and was
strenuously opposed by California. An interchange took place at
an A.F.B.F. board of directors' meeting between Blackburn of
California and Freudenthal of New Mexico.

Mr. Blackburn: . . . There is a bill before Congress to increase the tariff
on jute and jute buts [*sic*] 3¢ per pound. Chester tells me it has no chance
of passing in his judgment. I would like the consent of the Board that
Mr. Gray be authorized to oppose this measure. . . . We use 3,000,000
bags in California. These bags are made at the San Quentin prison.
Mr. Freudenthal: Before that suggestion is accepted, I want to say that

[20] Alex Johnson, Secretary of the California Farm Bureau, to the A.F.B.F.,
October 2, 1939.
[21] *A.F.B.F. Official News Letter,* October 10, 1939.

it is apparently to the disinterest of the cotton farmers. We cannot see why you cannot use our bags rather than imported bags.

Mr. Blackburn: We have tried to use them, but they are not nearly as satisfactory as jute bags.

Mr. O'Neal: I do not think they will put any tariff on jute.

Mr. Blackburn: I would like to call attention to the Board that the only request is that the situation remain status quo. I merely ask that you do not penalize by adding 3¢ additional per pound to jute. . . .Consumption is all intra-state.

Mr. Freudenthal: I have no objection to the A.F.B.F. taking the position as last outlined by Mr. Blackburn.[22]

As has been pointed out above, O'Neal himself believed that cotton farmers had more to gain by supporting the main principle of tariff reduction than by pursuing such trifling gains as a tariff on jute. He was aware, however, that neither was there solid Southern sectional support for this line of reasoning (for the Southern textile interests in particular opposed it) nor was there solid Democratic Party support for it. "As you know," he wrote, "many Democrats are as jealous of tariff protection as the members from the other side of the House, and therefore I am unable to agree with you that 'such a splendid opportunity presents itself for tariff revision in the Congress.' 'Splendid opportunity' is more apparent than real."[23]

There are indications, too, that the A.A.A. program itself was beginning to influence some Southerners to turn away from their traditional free trade position to economic nationalism. It appeared that the maintenance of parity prices for agricultural products on the domestic market by means of the A.A.A. program was becoming more important than foreign trade to some Southern farmers. O'Neal himself, the most fervent advocate of both parity through the A.A.A. and of economic internationalism through the reciprocal trade program, did not believe that the two programs were at all incompatible. He was chided for inconsistency by George Peek, a convinced economic nationalist. "You cannot run with the hare and hunt with the hounds," wrote Peek to O'Neal.[24]

---

[22] A.F.B.F., *Minutes of the Board of Directors,* January 9-11, 1936.

[23] O'Neal to Leo A. La Grave, Vice-President of the Cotton Club of the Port of Mobile, January 31, 1936.

[24] Peek to O'Neal, May 13, 1943. Peek elucidated his views on the reciprocal trade program as follows: "You may have forgotten the fact that the idea of Parity (or as it was formerly expressed 'fair exchange value') between farm and industrial products originated with me and was developed with the assistance of General Johnson in the form of the brief, EQUALITY FOR AGRICULTURE. The heart of the whole argument was based upon the difference

Another illustration of the way sectional complexities affected tariff policy is found in the Northeastern dairy region. Dairy farmers generally were very much opposed to the reciprocal trade program,[25] yet New England farmers wished Canadian feed wheat as well as mill offals to be admitted to the United States without the imposition of the quota which was desired by Midwestern farmers.[26] Midwestern farmers thought such a quota desirable because it probably would cause a slight rise in the price of Midwestern feed grains, and this of course was the very reason why Northeastern farmers, as important users of feed grains, opposed the quota.

If there was not solid sectional or party support for the reciprocal trade program in the South and the Democratic Party, neither was there solid sectional or party opposition to it in the Midwest and Republican party. There was a growing group among Midwestern farm bureaus and younger Midwestern Farm Bureau leaders who favored positive support for a freer trade policy. The Ohio Farm Bureau, which was not typical of Midwestern farm bureaus anyway, was outspoken in its opposition to the protective tariff system. Its president declared: "Farmers must recognize the need and necessity for almost a complete reversal of their traditional attitudes and also [of their] political support of the protective tariff system as it has existed."[27]

More subtle and probably more significant differences in Mid-

---

between world and domestic prices. We took the position that there were but two remedies. One, raise farm prices to fair exchange value with industrial prices. The other, reduce industrial prices to the level of world prices. The position of the Farm Bureau throughout the years had been that we should attempt the former. The working out of the Trade Agreements is in the direction of the latter. In other words, the Farm Bureau in its resolution is reversing the position it has maintained for twenty years—and I cannot believe that it understood what it was doing, in spite of your assurance to the contrary." Peek to O'Neal, May 16, 1943.

[25] Charles W. Holman, Secretary of the National Co-operative Milk Producers' Federation, "How Trade Agreements Affect the Welfare of Dairy Farmers," a speech delivered to the National Farm Institute, February 18, 1938 (copy in A.F.B.F., O'Neal Papers). In 1940 O'Neal indignantly denounced what he considered to be efforts by the Dairymen's League to get the Co-op Council to pass a resolution condemning the reciprocal trade treaties. Since, however, action by the Co-op Council had to be unanimously approved, such efforts were blocked, according to O'Neal's informants, by the cotton co-ops. O'Neal to J. F. Porter, January 30, 1940; and Porter to Cordell Hull, January 24, 1940 (copies in A.F.B.F., O'Neal Papers).

[26] N. E. Dodd, Director of the Western Division of the A.A.A., to O'Neal, February 14, 1940.

[27] Perry L. Green to O'Neal, May 29, 1941.

western points of view regarding foreign trade were those between
the two most powerful Midwestern Farm Bureau states, Illinois and
Iowa. There was much more sentiment for freer trade in Iowa than
in Illinois. The relatively internationalist persuasion of the *Des
Moines Register* as compared to the *Chicago Tribune* accounts for
some of it. Probably *Wallace's Farmer* and some of the staff at the
Iowa State College at Ames were also influential in this direction.
As early as 1938, Allan B. Kline, then Vice-President of the Iowa
Farm Bureau, had stated his position favoring a lowering of tariffs.[28]

Earl Smith probably represented with fair accuracy the view
of the majority of the Midwestern Farm Bureau leaders, particularly those of his own generation. And he was very wary indeed of
weakening the protective tariff system. But O'Neal could count
upon one quality in Earl Smith. He was a man who respected facts,
when he was sure of their authenticity. Unlike the old-style evan-
gelical agrarian leaders, he took pride in making his decisions on
the basis of logic rather than emotion. It was probably chiefly with
the hope of winning Earl Smith and other leaders like him that
O'Neal proposed an objective study of the reciprocal trade program.

Since it was chiefly the uncertain Midwestern farmers that O'Neal
had to win, it was fortunate that he could get intellectual support
from one of their own universities, the Iowa State College at Ames.
For political advice O'Neal turned most often to a Southern college
president, Dr. L. N. Duncan of the land-grant college at Auburn,
Alabama, but for advice on economics O'Neal turned elsewhere, as
he himself wrote to Dr. Duncan:

> Since I have been up here [A.F.B.F. headquarters in Chicago] I have
> been getting my economic advice mostly from Ames, Cornell, the Uni-
> versity of Illinois, University of Missouri, and so on. . . . Just recently I
> had Dr. Schultz, Head of the Economics Department of Iowa State Col-
> lege, analyze the reciprocal trade treaties for me. Because of the data he
> assembled for me, our farmers were convinced that the treaties should
> be continued. The factual data I use must be beyond question, for I have
> to submit so many letters and statements to Congress that are unquestion-
> able as to facts.[29]

[28] Saloutos and Hicks, *op. cit.*, p. 529. Kline was elected president of the
A.F.B.F. in 1947.
[29] O'Neal to Duncan, December 19, 1939. In the 1920's "the professor" to the
A.F.B.F. was George Warren of Cornell. In the 1930's the A.F.B.F. continued
to look to him as the authority on monetary matters, but for advice on other
economic policies, O'Neal, although himself a Southerner, seems to have depended almost entirely on economists at the Midwestern colleges and universities, as well as on those in the U.S. Department of Agriculture.

The official arrangement for the research into the effects of the reciprocal trade treaties was made in a contract between the administration at the Iowa State College and the A.F.B.F.[30]

Dr. Theodore W. Schultz was asked to appear both before the board of directors and before the annual convention in December, 1939, to present and explain the findings of his research. That the board members grasped the wider implications of the reciprocal trade program, beyond narrow commodity interests, is evidenced by Earl Smith's summing-up of Schultz's report:

Mr. Smith: Taking all countries with whom we have trade agreements, there have been increased exports, industrial and agricultural, in 1937 and 1938, over 1933-35 of 61%. In the case of all non-agreement countries our exports have increased 37.9% and our imports have increased 37%. In other words, the imports into this country are substantially on the same percentage as from the agreement countries, while our exports have gone up nearly twice as much to the trade-agreement countries—61.2% as compared to 37.9%. Another thing that impresses me—dealing directly with agricultural products I don't see that we have much advantage one way or the other. The tremendous increase in industrial exports gives agriculture indirect benefit, which is substantial, through increased employment and consumption of our agricultural products.

Dr. Schultz: You have stated it excellently.[31]

It was on the basis, therefore, of an understanding of the benefits of the reciprocal trade program to the over-all national economy, above sectional or special commodity interests, that the A.F.B.F. voted to endorse its continuance. As part of his campaign to secure this endorsement, O'Neal also had Secretary of State Cordell Hull speak at the annual meeting in December, 1939. He thought it advisable, however, to warn Hull not to talk too much, specifically, about the reciprocal trade program.

It was a real victory for O'Neal when, at this meeting, the A.F.B.F. adopted a resolution endorsing the proposal to extend the Reciprocal Trade Agreements Act. The adoption of this policy was based on a clear conception of the *national* interest, for the resolution goes on to point out the same thing that Earl Smith earlier had so succinctly summarized to the board of directors.[32] The resolution states, in part:

[30] R. E. Buchanan, Director of the Iowa Agricultural Experiment Station, to O'Neal, October 20, 1939; O'Neal to C. B. Murray, Treasurer of the Iowa State College, November 15, 1939.

[31] A.F.B.F., "Minutes of the Board of Directors, December 2, 1939," A.F.B.F., O'Neal Papers. These are the manuscript minutes, signed by the stenographer, from which the briefer printed minutes were prepared.

[32] This was to be expected, since Earl Smith was chairman of the resolutions committee.

The Federation recently sponsored a study by recognized economists of the economic effects of all important existing trade agreements. This study seems to reveal that there has been a substantially larger increase in exports to agreement than to non-agreement countries, and that there has not been any appreciable difference in the percentage of increase in imports from agreement and non-agreement countries. Many factors have no doubt contributed to this increased trade, including our gold policy and a general upturn in world business. From all facts thus far available, it appears that while the greatest portion of increased exports has been in industrial products, from which agriculture has only indirectly benefited, yet this study, together with other information available to the Federation, reveals that the net effect of the agreements has been helpful rather than hurtful.[33]

From the mature economic reasoning demonstrated in this resolution, it would seem that farmers had gone a long way from the time when tariff policy with them was largely an outgrowth of Civil War emotions. Moreover, the A.F.B.F. had fulfilled a function of "educating" its members in the true sense, for O'Neal had sought scholarly and objective research into the facts upon which the policy should be based, and then had seen to it that the results of this research were made known. Incidentally, O'Neal attempted not only to educate the members of his organization in this matter, but he sent copies of the Iowa State College report (or summaries of it) to various persons and agencies of influence, including President Roosevelt, the U.S. Department of Agriculture, Senator Scott Lucas of Illinois, Eugene Butler (editor of the *Progressive Farmer*), Congressman Walter M. Pierce, Congressman Ernest Lundeen, and others.[34] And, of course, he used it as an important basis of his statement at the Congressional hearings on the extension of the reciprocal trade program.

The Farm Bureau's resolution endorsing the reciprocal trade program was not as strong as O'Neal would have wished it to be, for it contained two qualifications and a specific exception. The same "escape clause" to protect parity which the A.F.B.F. had previously insisted upon was repeated. This was that "no concessions be made which might have the effect of reducing or holding the domestic price of any agricultural commodity below the parity level."[35] Further, the resolution proposed an amendment especially favored by the Illinois Agricultural Association, namely, that no agreement

---

[33] A.F.B.F., *Resolutions of the Annual Meeting*, 1939.
[34] Covering letters are in A.F.B.F., O'Neal Papers. They are also to be found in the Correspondence of the Secretary of Agriculture, National Archives. President Roosevelt's letter of thanks is printed in the Congressional hearings.
[35] "Resolutions, 1939," *A.F.B.F. Official News Letter*, December 11, 1939; *ibid.*, February 13, 1940.

be consummated unless it had the approval not only of the Secretary of State as the existing law provided, but of the Secretaries of Commerce and Agriculture as well. Specifically, the resolutions of 1939 pointed out that it would be extremely difficult to negotiate a trade agreement with Argentina which would not be "fraught with grave danger to American agriculture, for the reason that the bulk of Argentine exports are directly competitive with the products of American farms."[36] The State Department was warned that any concessions made to Argentina which might reduce or hold the domestic price of any agricultural commodity below the parity level would force the American farmers to condemn such an agreement and would seriously detract from their support of this fundamental policy of foreign trade.[37] The proposed trade agreements with Chile and Uruguay, according to the A.F.B.F. resolution, fell into the same category as that with Argentina.

In A.F.B.F. parlance, the escape clause and other qualifications constituted only "proper safeguards." The only reason that they did not fatally vitiate the resolution is that it was not the "safeguards" but the advantages to farmers of the treaties themselves that O'Neal emphasized, as for example in his testimony before the Ways and Means Committee of Congress in January, 1940.

In his appearance before the committee, O'Neal emphasized the conclusion of the Iowa State College report that the over-all result of trade agreements had been beneficial to American agriculture.[38] The statement was as strong as he could possibly make it, though naturally he had to state the qualifications which his organization imposed. During the question period, he continued to maintain a strong position on freer trade, though in typical O'Neal fashion he was often incoherent and rambling but always politically astute. O'Neal had absolutely no awe for congressmen, to whom he frequently addressed such remarks: "Here is what I mean, brother." Or again, "I can see why an industrialist in a part of the country where you come from just doesn't understand agriculture. . . ." Or to another, "But you can't get into your mind—I don't know why you can't understand how efficient we are and how we just simply cannot absorb a normal production of cotton."[39] It was apparently

---

[36] *Ibid.*

[37] *Ibid.*

[38] U.S. House, *Hearings, Extension of Reciprocal Trade Agreements Act. Part 2*, pp. 1668-1722. The report of the Iowa State College group is printed in full in these hearings at the request of the committee, though O'Neal had originally requested only that the summary be printed.

[39] *Ibid.*

O'Neal's conviction that congressmen were the servants of the people, and that he was there to instruct them as to what they ought to do for the people, especially farmers.

O'Neal was not willing to agree with the congressman who wished to protect agriculture to the extent of placing an embargo on competitive agricultural products when the domestic price was below parity.[40] When questioned directly about the amendment suggested by the A.F.B.F. (to the effect that any future reciprocal trade agreements should be unanimously approved by the Secretaries of Commerce and Agriculture, as well as by the Secretary of State), O'Neal tried to soft-pedal the amendment by implying that this was in effect being done already.[41]

After Ed O'Neal's appearance before the Ways and Means Committee, Cordell Hull wrote him a letter of thanks. Below the typewritten formal letter is written by hand, "a marvelous statement. C. H."[42] O'Neal's own reaction was: "I enjoyed the ordeal very much. . . ."[43]

While of course saying nothing of it publicly, O'Neal felt shackled by the compromises he was forced to make in order to promote agricultural unity on the foreign trade question. To J. F. Porter he wrote privately: "The Pat Harrison committee reported out the trade treaties without our amendment, and from all I can hear it is going to be difficult to get our amendment in on the floor. It is too bad that we are in the position we are now in. It is very embarrassing to me. I know at heart most of our leaders are for the trade treaties, yet we are estopped from advocating them. I think it is a mistake."[44]

The amendment O'Neal referred to was the one favored by the Illinois Agricultural Association—that is, the requirement that any reciprocal trade treaty should have the approval of the Secretaries of Agriculture and Commerce as well as the Secretary of State. O'Neal then made an attempt to persuade Earl Smith not to oppose the reciprocal trade program if the amendment were not accepted by Congress. In a typed note to "Mr. Smith," unsigned but obviously from O'Neal, the plea is made: "I think the right thing to do is to honestly carry out the purpose of the resolution in the statement but so word it that no possible interpretation could be

[40] *Ibid.*, p. 1691.
[41] *Ibid.*, p. 1697.
[42] Hull to O'Neal, January 26, 1940.
[43] O'Neal to Theodore W. Schultz, January 31, 1940.
[44] O'Neal to Porter, March 12, 1940.

made that if they wouldn't put in the amendment you were fighting or going to fight reciprocal trade treaties; rather that you were put in a position that you could not give active support to, nor adequate defense of trade treaties, if they went that road."[45]

When the Reciprocal Trade Agreements program was extended by Congress in April, 1940, for three more years, the A.F.B.F. amendment was not included, nor, in fact, had it even been voted upon. The unsuccessful La Follette amendment, which proposed the establishment of a board consisting of the Secretaries of State, Commerce, and Agriculture, who would have the authority to *negotiate* the treaties, went further, as the *A.F.B.F. Official News Letter* was careful to point out, than the A.F.B.F. amendment which proposed only that the three Secretaries have authority to *approve* the treaties.

The significance of O'Neal's success in winning even the qualified support of his organization for the principle of reciprocal trade goes beyond economic policy. The reciprocal trade program was the symbol of internationalism in the early New Deal. The A.F.B.F.'s swing away from its high tariff policy of the 1920's toward the re- ciprocal trade program of the New Deal was a crucial step by which the organization turned from isolationism toward internationalism in foreign policy. In 1940 the A.F.B.F. dramatically reversed its position on armaments from that of the year before (which favored limitation of armaments to the reasonable requirements of national defense) to an endorsement of Roosevelt's rearmament program. Also in 1940, when Lend Lease was still under the attack of isola- tionists, the A.F.B.F. endorsed the policy of extending aid to Britain and her allies.[46] As Roosevelt led the nation further and further away from isolationism, the main elements of his foreign policy were endorsed by the A.F.B.F.[47]

---

[45] The note is attached to a letter from Senator Vandenberg to O'Neal, March 29, 1940, referring to the Farm Bureau's proposed amendment to the bill on trade treaties. It is accompanied by a note from Earl Smith to O'Neal, April 25, 1940, saying that the correspondence had been buried. All are in A.F.B.F. O'Neal Papers, file marked "U.S. Senate, 1939."

[46] A.F.B.F., *Resolutions of the Annual Meeting*, 1940.

[47] The sectional line-up on tariff policy revealed at an A.F.B.F. board of directors' meeting in June, 1949 (which the writer was permitted to attend), showed a contrast with that of the earlier period. At the 1949 meeting, an amendment which would have tended to cripple the reciprocal trade program was defeated by a coalition of Midwesterners and Southerners, the Midwestern group being split on this question. The amendment, endorsing the "peril point" principle, was proposed by Roberts of New Mexico in the interest of protect- ing cotton farmers against Egyptian cotton. It was seconded by Gillespie of

the state of Washington, who explained that Washington's berry market was being ruined by Canadian berries and Italian cherries. President Allan B. Kline of Iowa succinctly stated the case for free trade, in opposition to the amendment. When Gillespie urged as the reason why Washington state berries needed protection—the fact that Canada could produce berries more cheaply—Kline's remark was that the purpose of trade is to exchange with an area that has a production advantage. It was Romeo Short of Arkansas, however, who presented the really impassioned plea against crippling limitations on the reciprocal trade program. Short was a veteran of the 1939-40 fight for the extension of the reciprocal trade program, which he believed could not have been won had not the A.F.B.F. pushed it. Some insight into old battles may be gained also from the opinions of the two leaders, Ed O'Neal and Earl Smith (after their retirement) on the succeeding president of the A.F.B.F. Each stated to the writer that Allan Kline was an internationalist, but O'Neal said so with approval, Earl Smith with disapproval.

CHAPTER X

The Beginning of the Break
with the New Deal

After the Presidential election of 1936, there began a titanic struggle between the U.S. Department of Agriculture and the A.F.B.F. To say "began" is not precisely correct, for it is impossible to determine exactly when it started. By coeval processes, the Department of Agriculture consulted less freely about farm policy with the Farm Bureau, and the leaders of the Farm Bureau became more insistent in their demands that it was their right to be consulted. The role of the Extension Service was a central issue in this conflict. The Department of Agriculture sought to lessen its early dependence on the Extension Service for the local administration of the New Deal farm programs and to establish straight-line administration through agencies of the Department. At the same time, the A.F.B.F. attempted to place the administration of practically everything under the Extension Service.

Previous to the New Deal, federal aid to agriculture had been chiefly through grants-in-aid for agricultural education rather than through direct action. And agricultural education was (and is) carried out chiefly through the Extension Service administered by the land-grant colleges. The key figure in this system is the county agent, who carries the expert technical advice of the colleges to the local farmers. Federal control over the county agents has been negligible under the decentralized system by which the Extension Service has traditionally operated. While the procedure by which a county agent is appointed varies somewhat from state to state, the appointing procedure most frequently followed is for the state Extension Service to recommend qualified candidates, from among whom the local sponsoring body appoints the agent. Final approval must be given by the director of the Federal Extension Service, who is an officer of the U.S. Department of Agriculture, but this has usually been a formal matter only.[1] Until the Farm Bureau was separated from the Extension Service in 1954, the local sponsoring body was in some cases the county farm bureau. However, legal ties were not always as binding as informal reciprocal understandings between the Farm Bureau and the Extension Service.

The new agricultural programs undertaken by the federal government during the period of the New Deal were chiefly "action" programs designed to give economic aid to farmers, as distinguished from the traditional educational programs. "Action" agencies were accordingly set up in order to carry these programs out. In the beginning, the most important of these, the A.A.A., worked through the county agents of the Extension Service.

However, the mushroom growth of agencies of the new type eventually brought about basic changes in the structure of the federal Department of Agriculture, and in the relationships of the Extension Service to the new programs. Some of the new action agencies, such as the Rural Resettlement Administration, the Farm Credit Administration, and the Rural Electrification Administration, were originally outside the Department of Agriculture. But after 1936 these outside agencies were gradually brought within the Department, and moreover responsibilities for the local administration of the A.A.A. were withdrawn from the county agents of the Extension Service. Thus the administration of "action" programs, as distinct from educational programs, was increasingly centralized in the federal Department of Agriculture, which reached farmers directly through its "action" agencies. The A.A.A., for instance, had its own county offices, and its own local farmer committeemen. While the Farm Bureau was in some cases able to dominate the farmer committeemen of the A.A.A.,[2] the influence of the Farm Bureau with a centralized agency was not likely to be as strong as with a decentralized agency like the Extension Service, since the organization and development of the Farm Bureau virtually paralleled that of the Extension Service.

In 1936 the A.F.B.F. detected signs that its own influence with the federal Department of Agriculture was beginning to wane, and that simultaneously other agencies of the Department were gaining in importance relative to the Extension Service.

---

[1] Block, *op. cit.*, pp. 7-8.
[2] *Ibid.*, pp. 16-17.

No single event can be pinpointed as precipitating the struggle between the A.F.B.F. and the Department of Agriculture, but two incidents epitomize it. One was a visit by Ed O'Neal and another Farm Bureau leader (probably Earl Smith) to Secretary Wallace and Paul H. Appleby, Assistant to the Secretary, at the offices of the Department of Agriculture, at which the Farm Bureau leaders made the demand that the Department make no major decisions without consulting them. Wallace made no such promise, although he gave them no direct answer. Since this was soon after the triumphant re-election of Roosevelt in 1936, in which some Farm Bureau leaders had given him strong support, it appeared to Administration officials that the Farm Bureau leaders were implying that they had delivered the votes and now wished their *quid pro quo*. Roosevelt had pre-emptorily refused an equivalent demand by John L. Lewis, and the Department of course was no more willing to accede to this one.[3]

In the same year, the Department of Agriculture sent Howard R. Tolley, then Administrator of the A.A.A., to the annual convention of the Association of Land-Grant Colleges and Universities to make a speech thanking the gentlemen of the Extension Service for the aid they had given the Department in the administration of the A.A.A. and informing them that their assistance in this connection would not be required in the future. This was a hard blow to the Farm Bureau, for not only was its old ally the Extension Service deprived of important powers, but the Farm Bureau had not even been consulted about it. Afterward O'Neal called upon M. L. Wilson to inquire if he had known that the Department was going to take this step. When Wilson said that he *had* known about it in advance, O'Neal complained that the Department should not make such decisions without prior consultation with the Farm Bureau, or at least without notifying them in advance. O'Neal thought that it was not right that the Farm Bureau leadership should have to learn of such decisions from the newspapers.[4]

---

[3] Appleby, personal interview, August 18, 1959. Henry A. Wallace, when questioned about this incident in a personal interview on August 27, 1959, did not remember this specific incident, but thought it was quite in keeping with the trend of Farm Bureau demands.

[4] Wilson, personal interview, August 18, 1959. The *Proceedings of the Association of Land-Grant Colleges and Universities* (1936) show that Tolley made two speeches at this convention. One, to the general session, was entitled "The Farmer, the College, the Department of Agriculture—Their Changing Relationships" (pp. 70-76); the other, delivered to the subsection on Extension work, was entitled "The Conservation Program and the Extension Service" (pp.

In contrast to the situation early in 1936, when the Farm Bureau was profoundly satisfied with its relationship with the Department of Agriculture and in particular with Secretary Wallace, between 1936 and 1940 O'Neal frequently expressed resentment over the fact that the Department did "policy things" without talking with the Farm Bureau leaders about them. O'Neal felt that the Farm Bureau's advice should be asked, though the Secretary of Agriculture would not have to follow that advice unless he wanted to. Thus Farm Bureau leaders believed that the Department of Agriculture was denying them what was perhaps the most vital right which a national farm organization could possess—the right to be consulted in the making of agricultural policy.

The first Administration to grant such a right in any significant degree to the leaders of farm organizations had been that of Franklin D. Roosevelt, whose Secretary of Agriculture had called in farm leaders to assist in formulating the Agricultural Adjustment Act of 1933 and the Soil Conservation Act of 1936, and who had consulted less formally with the Farm Bureau leaders on other occasions. The recognition thus accorded the Farm Bureau had been a most significant factor in promoting the prestige and influence of the organization. Now it appeared that this recognition was being progressively withdrawn by the same Administration and even under the same Secretary of Agriculture who had originally granted it.

This struggle between the Department of Agriculture and the Farm Bureau remained chiefly underground, only occasionally coming to the surface in isolated incidents or specific conflicts, such as those over the Farm Credit Administration and the Farm Security Administration. Most of the time the relations between the Department of Agriculture and the Farm Bureau remained superficially much as usual, except for a perceptible waning of the old mutual confidence. Much of the time they continued to work together on those policies which both supported. It was not until 1940 that the lid really came off.

Involved in the major struggle for power were many sorts of conflicts, the threads of which are exceedingly tangled. Among the

190-91). The printed version of neither speech says exactly what Tolley is reported to have said, but since only a brief abstract of the speech to the Extension section appears in the *Proceedings* it is quite probably this speech to which Wilson referred. In any case, the general theme of both speeches is in keeping with the incident as reported.

major sources of conflict were: (1) differences in concepts of the proper role of the Department of Agriculture; (2) the issue of centralization versus decentralization of power in the administration of the federal farm programs; (3) increasing divergence over the substance of the farm program; (4) rivalry between government agencies ("empire-building"); (5) rivalry between farm organizations; (6) partisan politics; (7) the influence of personalities; and (8) fundamental differences over how farm policy should be made in a democracy.

The A.F.B.F.'s concept of the Department of Agriculture was based upon a premise which was becoming more and more unacceptable to the Administration. This premise, which applied to all agricultural agencies whether federal or state, was explicitly stated by O'Neal soon after he became president of the A.F.B.F. in 1931. He said then: "Thinking farmers have a jealous regard for these institutions, feeling that they in very deed belong to them and that these institutions were created for the purpose of serving the farmers alone. In no case do we farmers question the right of the Department of Commerce to aggressively serve business nor of the Department of Labor to vigorously promote the welfare of the group it represents. In turn, we must demand that those serving agriculture be anxiously concerned only in the welfare of the group they represent."[5] This obviously was a "clientele" concept of the departments of government.

The more politically sophisticated members of the Administration, however, looked upon themselves as representative of the chief executive, who in turn was the one official elected by the vote of all the people and presumably therefore the representative of the interests of all. Even apart from the fact that at least some of the officers of the Department of Agriculture conceived its role broadly as that of serving the general public, rather than narrowly that of promoting the interests of farmers alone, there were two interest groups other than farmers which felt that they had special claims for consideration by the Department of Agriculture. These were: (1) consumers and (2) processors of agricultural products. While during the early New Deal the Farm Bureau considered that processors were the worst enemy of the farm program, there was never any suspicion on the Farm Bureau's part that the Department of Agriculture was unduly protecting the interests of this group. During the latter days of the New Deal, however, there were many

---

[5] *A.F.B.F. Official News Letter,* September 15, 1931.

expressions of alarm over what was called in Farm Bureau circles "consumer dominance" in the Department of Agriculture.

The second major source of conflict, the issue of centralization as against decentralization, is basic in explaining the "divorce" of the A.A.A. from the Extension Service in 1936.[6] The establishment of a new relationship was not, of course, a simple matter of making a speech at a Land-Grant College Association meeting, though the land-grant college people apparently held Tolley responsible for it. In order to achieve the goal, the state and local A.A.A. committees had to be divorced from informal domination by the Farm Bureau as well, and this was a long, drawn-out process. Trouble centered in the state of Iowa, which seems to have been made a test case by the Department of Agriculture in its attempt to wrench the A.A.A. (and other action programs) out from under Extension Service-Farm Bureau domination and place the administration of them instead under the more direct control of the federal Department of Agriculture. As early as 1935, when Dr. A. G. Black was administrator of the corn-hog section of the A.A.A., this struggle had come intermittently into the open. For instance, the *Cedar Rapids Gazette* declared: "The Farm Bureau was ignored when the state corn and hog committee was named by Dr. A. G. Black and it again was 'slapped in the face,' so organization leaders say, when district fieldmen carefully were selected last fall from men who are not active Farm Bureau boosters, and when Farm Bureau leaders such as Allan B. Kline of Vinton, Paul P. Stewart of Maynard, and others were summarily dismissed by Dr. Black, without explanation."[7]

The issue of centralization as against decentralization of power was a genuine one in this struggle. The Department of Agriculture held, logically, that it had been charged with the responsibility for carrying out certain programs, and that it could not discharge its responsibilities through an agency like the Extension Service, over which the federal Department had only nominal authority and over which the states had the real authority. The Department of Agriculture had turned to the Extension Service for assistance in administering the Agricultural Adjustment Act in 1933 only as an emergency measure. Conversely, the Farm Bureau, while convinced of the necessity of a national program for agriculture, sought to

---

[6] The phrase is that of Charles M. Hardin, "The Bureau of Agricultural Economics Under Fire: A Study in Valuation Conflicts," *Journal of Farm Economics*, XXVIII (August, 1946), 645.

[7] Article by Ray Anderson, *Cedar Rapids Gazette*, May 10, 1935, p. 20.

maintain the traditional agrarian opposition to the centralization of power in government by insisting that the *administration* of federal programs should be decentralized. To Farm Bureau leaders the Extension Service seemed the ideal agency for such purposes. The cynical explanation that the Extension Service was often allied with the Farm Bureau, though true, ignores the deep-rooted value which farm people placed upon the cherished Jeffersonian concept of decentralization of power.

The land-grant colleges (and the Extension Services associated with them) were divided, in some cases uncertain, about whether they wished all the powers in connection with the federal action programs which the Department of Agriculture was apparently determined to take away from them and which the Farm Bureau was equally determined they should retain and even expand. The Extension Services of the Southern colleges and universities were most favorable to administering the action programs; the Northeastern colleges were generally opposed; while the Midwestern colleges held intermediate shades of opinion.

A crisis that occurred in 1936 throws light on some of the complex relationships involved. In that year, when the Supreme Court invalidated the original Agricultural Adjustment Act, and the Soil Conservation and Domestic Allotment legislation was enacted in its place, the Farm Bureau tried to have a requirement included in the act to the effect that the agency to administer the plan should be the land-grant college in the state or such other state agency as might be approved by the Secretary. This provision was not included in the legislation as passed by Congress.

At about the same time, a cut of 25 per cent was scheduled in the federal appropriations for the Extension Service. Actually, it was proposed that the total funds available would be increased through an additional appropriation of $1,000,000 from Bankhead-Jones funds. In spite of this, federal grants to the Extension Service would have been decreased in 22 states because Bankhead-Jones funds were allocated to the states on the basis of farm population, whereas the supplemental Smith-Lever funds were allocated on the basis of rural population. O'Neal maintained that he would continue to fight against the proposed cut in appropriations, but if this fight were lost, he thought a primary reason would be "the position you fellows have taken" on the administration of the Soil Conservation Act.[8] Nevertheless, O'Neal gave the assurance that he had done his best

---

[8] O'Neal to A. R. Mann, February 25, 1936.

to retain all the funds, "in spite of the reaction that had set in on the Hill."[9]

A. R. Mann, chairman of the executive committee of the Association of Land-Grant Colleges and Universities, explained to O'Neal the position of the colleges. This was that while there was unanimous desire on the part of the land-grant colleges to handle the educational and scientific aspects of the program, "many of the institutions take a strong stand against assuming responsibility for the regulatory and control features."[10] While Mann did not state it explicitly, this was particularly true of the Eastern colleges, from which he himself came. Northeastern farmers generally, including the Farm Bureau members, had been opposed to the A.A.A. To ask the Eastern colleges to administer the successor to the A.A.A., particularly the regulatory features of such a program, would make them very unpopular with farmers in their own area.

While O'Neal particularly blamed the Eastern college leaders, he also deplored a similar position taken by some college administrators in the Midwest.[11] He was sure that "the Southern and Far Western Extension fellows see the vital necessity of their administering the law."[12]

Apparently O'Neal asked several Extension officials to appear before the A.F.B.F. board of directors to explain their unwillingness to accept the responsibility of administering the new program for agriculture. At any rate, at the first quarterly meeting of the board following the incident, he welcomed as guests Director Warburton, head of the U.S. Extension Service, Director Bliss of Iowa, and Director Creel of Nevada. Then, in the bluntest language possible, he told them they ought to know who their friends were and who their enemies were by that time.[13] The context of this statement makes unmistakably clear what O'Neal meant:

We are honored here by having as guests, Director Warburton, Director Bliss of Iowa and Director Creel of Nevada. I would like to say frankly that we asked for their co-operation and the Land Grant Colleges in the administration of the new Soil Conservation Act. We felt they were the logical agencies to administer the act in the various states. We stood for their appropriation bill and felt that they should have stood by us in

---

[9] *Ibid.*

[10] Mann to O'Neal, February 25, 1936.

[11] O'Neal to Mann, February 28, 1936; and O'Neal to R. K. Bliss, Extension director in Iowa, March 4, 1936. This last letter is marked "don't send," and both the original and the carbon are in the O'Neal Papers.

[12] O'Neal to Mann, February 28, 1936.

[13] A.F.B.F., *Minutes of the Board of Directors,* March 5-7, 1936.

our position that this measure should designate the Land Grant Colleges as the administrative agency in the states. They ought to know who are their friends and who are their enemies by this time. . . .

We would like to have a word from some of you gentlemen.[14]

Bliss admitted that there had been differences of opinion within the land-grant colleges about how far the colleges should go in the regulatory work and the compliance work. However, he insisted that insofar as the special committee of the Extension Service (with which he was associated) was concerned, the Extension Services of the country had not "had the slightest thing to do with the elimination of agricultural colleges in the wording of the act."[15] Bliss thought that there was not one college in the country that would not want to have the educational and research work in connection with the program, but that this had been misunderstood.

Director Creel's remark was simply: "I was out in Nevada and did not know what was going on."[16]

Director Warburton thought that what happened was that some of the deans of the colleges sent telegrams to their senators and representatives before the meeting of the special committee of which Director Bliss spoke.[17]

Two years later at least one Midwestern land-grant college made its position crystal-clear. The Iowa State College at Ames made a study of the relationships of the land-grant college to federal activities in agriculture as a result of the introduction of the action programs of the New Deal. The issue was whether the college (and the Extension Service) should adhere to its traditional function of education only, or whether it should undertake administration in connection with the action programs. The conclusion was unequivocal. "The college not only wants no executive responsibility for the fulfilment of a program, but it must insist that none be imposed on it."[18] On the other hand, it wished to be entrusted with complete control of the agricultural education and research pertinent to the programs of direct action, or at least it wished a guarantee from both federal and state governments not to operate in these spheres without its complete co-operation.[19] Further, the bulletin declared,

---

[14] *Ibid.*

[15] *Ibid.*

[16] *Ibid.*

[17] *Ibid.*

[18] "The Role of the Land-Grant College in Governmental Agricultural Programs," *Iowa State College Bulletin*, XXXVIII (June 8, 1938), 12.

[19] *Ibid.*

the college's usefulness to government and to society depended upon keeping inviolate its reputation for integrity and objectivity. The implication was that too deep an involvement in action programs might endanger this reputation for objectivity.[20] It should be noted, however, that the college point of view might not be entirely in accord with that of the county agents, who are reported to have been somewhat more reluctant to relinquish responsibility for local administration of the action programs.

While the developing conflict between the Department of Agriculture and the Farm Bureau appears chiefly as a struggle for power, there might have been no power conflict had not a widening divergence of views developed over the substance of the programs. Once the extreme need for emergency programs in the early New Deal period was past, agreement on more permanent programs was much more difficult to obtain. The early A.A.A. and other similar programs had been based on the spirit if not the letter of McNary-Haugenism, in which Farm Bureau members had been educated for years, and which they thoroughly understood. If it is assumed that the New Deal program for agriculture had three facets—relief, recovery, and reform—the Farm Bureau went enthusiastically along on the first two of them, and balked on the third. Farm Bureau people were the repository of the old American values of the homestead era. They were innately resistant to reforms which went counter to these values, particularly when they were proposed not by one of their own farm people, like Henry A. Wallace, but by an urban liberal like Rex Tugwell. When the Rural Resettlement Administration (and its successor, the Farm Security Administration)[21] confined its activities primarily to rural relief, the Farm Bureau let it fairly much alone. But when the F.S.A. embarked on an aggressive program of reform, the Farm Bureau went on the warpath.

A basic assumption of Farm Bureau people, which was challenged by the F.S.A., was that the best possible system of land tenure was that of private, individual ownership. This principle was taken so much for granted that it was not even mentioned in the A.F.B.F. resolutions of 1934, which summarized the land utilization policies of the Farm Bureau. In fact it was not until President Roosevelt's Committee on Farm Tenancy made its report in 1937

---

[20] *Ibid.*, p. 14.

[21] The Farm Security Administration (usually known as the F.S.A.) evolved out of the Rural Resettlement Administration, which was established in 1935 with Rex Tugwell as administrator. It originated primarily as a rural relief agency, to aid the farm families in the lowest income group.

that the A.F.B.F. felt called upon to defend this principle. The report of the President's committee began with an expression of alarm over the increasing incidence of tenancy, then stated categorically: "The land policy adopted by this country, under which title to practically all of the agricultural land of the Nation passed to private owners in fee simple absolute, has proved defective as a means of keeping the land in the ownership of those who work it."[22] The report recommended that the federal government purchase land and sell it under long-term contracts to operating farmers, who would not, however, be allowed to repay all the principal and obtain title to the land until after 20 years. Thus it was hoped that speculation, ownership by non-farmers, and uneconomic subdivisions might be prevented. While the report in general favored family-size farms, it suggested that co-operative groups might in some cases be aided to acquire land by purchase or long lease for subleasing to group members.[23]

The Farm Bureau's insistence upon the fee simple ownership of farm land followed the tradition of those who fought for the homestead policy and other measures by which the public domain had passed into private ownership.

O'Neal, who was a member of the committee, stated that he could not be a signer of the report unless his objections to the proposed restrictions on the alienation of land were called to the attention of the reader. O'Neal's view was that more individuals should be aided to become landowners, as quickly as they had proved themselves to be good farmers.[24]

This conflict of views reappeared later in the fight between the Farm Bureau and the F.S.A., when the latter was alleged to be following the same policy regarding land ownership as that recommended by the President's committee.[25] That is, the F.S.A. was charged with refusing to allow its clients to pay off the principal of the mortgage indebtedness on their farms as soon as they were able, and thus refusing to allow them to gain title to their farms. A Southern Farm Bureau leader expressed the hostility of Farm Bu-

[22] *Farm Tenancy,* report of the President's Committee on Farm Tenancy, February, 1937. Prepared under the auspices of the National Resources Committee (Washington: Government Printing Office, 1937).
[23] *Ibid.*
[24] O'Neal to L. C. Gray, chairman of the President's committee, February 12, 1937, *ibid.,* appendix.
[25] U.S. House of Representatives, Subcommittee of the Committee on Appropriations, *Hearings on Agriculture Department Appropriation Bill for 1943. Part 2,* 77th Cong., 2d Sess., 1942, pp. 238-300, 618, 734-57.

reau leaders in his region to this sort of practice: "We thought the Farm Security Administration was to help tenants to become farm owners; we did not know it was to reform us." O'Neal himself had a genuine patriarchal interest in providing greater opportunities for the more poverty-stricken farmers of the South, but he wished these opportunities to be provided within the traditional social order. Farm Security officers thought it could not be done without changing the social order. The payment of poll taxes for Farm Security clients falls into the category of controversies of this nature.[26]

Rivalry among governmental agencies contributed to such conflicts as that over the F.S.A. In the case of both the Soil Conservation Service and the Rural Resettlement Administration it is fairly clear that at least part of the initiative for the A.F.B.F.'s policies toward these agencies came from some state Extension Services. For instance, Director Hutcheson of the Virginia Extension Service wrote to O'Neal expressing alarm over the regional offices of the Resettlement Administration, and said, "We are going to get Senator Byrd to help us." This was during a period when O'Neal was still calling Senator Byrd a reactionary.

In 1936 O'Neal gave a broad hint to Dean I. O. Schaub, Extension director in North Carolina, that he would like to see the recommendations of the Extension Committee on Resettlement, which had been made at the request of Tugwell, then head of the Resettlement Administration.[27] Schaub refused to give O'Neal a copy of the report, on the grounds that it would be unethical to do so, but he did divulge that it was the regional offices of the Resettlement Administration which disturbed the land-grant colleges. O'Neal could not have been too dissatisfied with the reply to his broadly hinted request, for Schaub concluded by expressing the hope that maybe Congress would find some way of calling for the report.[28]

O'Neal was also alarmed about the Soil Conservation Service, for he felt, rightly, that Hugh Bennett, who was head of it, "was driving right along" to keep it separate and increase its power and influence.[29] "As you know," wrote O'Neal to a college president, "I am

---

[26] Curiously enough, while active attack on the F.S.A. was led by certain Southern state farm bureau leaders, Southern senators were generally favorable to the F.S.A. It was the vote of Midwestern senators which virtually killed that agency.

[27] O'Neal to Schaub, August 31, 1936.

[28] Schaub to O'Neal, September 3, 1936.

[29] For a full analysis of the conflict over soil conservation, see Charles M. Hardin, *The Politics of Agriculture* (Glencoe, Illinois: The Free Press, 1952).

against all these things, running away from the proper foundation—
the Land Grant College."[30] He concluded with a reiteration of the
Virginian's statement: "We are going to get Senator Byrd to help
us."[31]

It was not only the Southern state colleges which feared that they
were being bypassed by the regional offices of the Soil Conservation Service and the Resettlement Administration. The Extension
directors of eight North-Central states protested, in 1937: "At the
present time there is a strong tendency on the part of certain bureaus and agencies in the U.S. Department of Agriculture to go
direct to the individual farmer, thus overlooking the possibilities of
making larger use of state and local agencies. . . ."[32] These Extension directors found the regional offices of the Soil Conservation
Service and the Resettlement Administration the most threatening
aspect of the agencies in question, for it was by means of the regional offices that a centralized system of administration, straight
from Washington to the farmer, could be maintained. The North-
Central directors explained and proposed:

> Without going into details we feel that the Soil Conservation Service
> through its regional offices largely nullifies the State co-operative agree-
> ments with the various colleges. How, for example, can a Land Grant
> College have much to say about the direction of the work in the State
> when a nearby powerful regional office with abundant funds and large
> technical personnel is operating at will across state lines. We strongly
> favor the development of the Soil Conservation Service on a state basis
> through an office established at the Land Grant College and working in
> close co-operation with the college.
>
> The arguments in regard to the Soil Conservation Service apply about
> equally well to rural resettlement. In Rural Resettlement we favor setting
> the work up on a state basis in close co-operation with the Land Grant
> College.[33]

It appears very much as if various land-grant college and Extension officials prodded O'Neal and the Farm Bureau into a battle
with other agencies, and then when the battle became rough and
the Farm Bureau wished to carry it further than the gentlemen of
the colleges and the Extension Service wished, the politicians of
academe began to run for cover. When the director of the Alabama

---

[30] O'Neal to Dr. T. O. Walton, President of the Texas A. and M. College,
September 1, 1936.

[31] *Ibid.*

[32] Statement signed by the Extension directors of Ohio, Indiana, Michigan,
Wisconsin, Missouri, Iowa, South Dakota, and the state leader of Nebraska,
"To the Department of Agriculture and the Land Grant College Co-ordinating
Committees," enclosed in a letter from R. K. Bliss to O'Neal, April 6, 1937.

[33] *Ibid.*

Extension Service, P. O. Davis, whom O'Neal called his "best buddy," informed O'Neal that the Southern directors of Extension had passed a resolution asking only that all educational work of the Department of Agriculture be done through the land-grant colleges, O'Neal was indignant: "We are leading this battle for you, but you are leaving us. I want to tell your Southerners you are leaving me out on a limb. You got this Byrd committee. Whether you made a mistake or not, you are leaving me on a limb."[34] After reminding Davis that in the national arena it was the Farm Bureau that was the target for sharpshooters, O'Neal threatened to get Davis up to Washington and let him "be shot."[35] (This was a reiteration probably of his earlier milder suggestion that P. O. Davis appear at a Congressional hearing and testify for the land-grant colleges.)

Senator John H. Bankhead of Alabama summed up the major interagency rivalries: "There are strong men in the government who want to reduce the work of the Extension Service and increase the authority of the F.S.A. On the other hand, there are strong men who want to enlarge the work of the Extension Service and reduce the authority of the F.S.A. There is another very strong group who want to give entire control and authority over all of these activities to the A.A.A."[36]

Rivalry between farm organizations was at least as important as interagency rivalry in explaining many of the issues of the late New Deal period. As the star of the Farm Bureau waned with the Department of Agriculture and the Roosevelt administration, that of another farm organization waxed. From being almost a voluntary outcast at the beginning of the New Deal period, the National Farmers' Union seems rapidly to have achieved prosperity and prestige (in Democratic circles) in the late New Deal period.

The Farm Bureau suspected the Administration of deliberately building up the Farmers' Union in order to have a strong lobby for the type of reform programs in agriculture which both the Administration and the Farmers' Union favored. (The fact that the Farm Bureau had developed out of just this sort of relationship with the Extension Service was overlooked. Anyway, that process probably had not been deliberate.) The Farmers' Union was the only national farm organization which would lobby for appropriations for

[34] Telephone conversation between Davis and O'Neal, January 30, 1942, A.F.B.F., O'Neal Papers (typescript).

[35] *Ibid.*

[36] Bankhead to Henry Hodo of Millport, Alabama, February 22, 1941, a copy of which Bankhead enclosed in a letter to P. O. Davis, February 22, 1941, and a copy of which Davis sent to O'Neal.

the F.S.A. On the other hand, federal funds were channeled through the F.S.A. into the Farmers' Union Grain Terminal Association, which became under M. W. Thatcher the strongest and most prosperous part of the Farmers' Union.

What the Farm Bureau officials considered as evidence that the resources of the F.S.A. were being used to build up the Farmers' Union was found in the loans made by the F.S.A. to its clients to enable them to purchase stock in co-operatives affiliated with the Farmers' Union. F.S.A. officials readily admitted that they did make such loans, but pointed out that the F.S.A. of course did not lay down any requirement that these co-operatives should be affiliated with any organization. Its interest was merely in the organization and development of farm co-operatives. In reply to a request from the Farm Bureau for information, the director of information for the F.S.A. stated that in the northern Great Plains area, the F.S.A. had made 9,696 loans to individual farmers to enable them to purchase stock in 99 local grain elevator associations, all of which were affiliated with the Farmers' Union Grain Terminal Association. Moreover, 9,216 loans had been made by the F.S.A. to enable individual rehabilitation borrowers to purchase preferred stock in the Farmers' Union Grain Terminal Association.[37]

This looked more like a plot than a coincidence to the Farm Bureau. Moreover, M. W. Thatcher, chairman of the Legislative Committee of the Farmers' Union, who was also general manager of the Farmers' Union Grain Terminal Association, had pointed with pride in his report to the fact that the F.S.A. had made such loans: "The Farm Security Administration has made loans to low-income farmers to enable them to participate in the purchase of preferred stock in our association."[38]

In allying itself with the National Farmers' Union, the F.S.A. entered the wars of agricultural politics, and invited political annihilation. The Farm Bureau accepted the invitation.[39]

---

[37] John Fischer, Director of Information of the F.S.A., to W. R. Ogg, Washington, D.C. [n.d.]. The date must have been late 1939 or early 1940. It is in the O'Neal files for 1939. This letter may be only a copy, for a note attached to it says that the original was returned to the Farm Bureau's Washington representative, Ogg, on April 17, 1940; yet the letter in the O'Neal files is on F.S.A. letterhead paper.

[38] "The Report to the Stockholders, Farmers' Union Grain Terminal Association, St. Paul, Minnesota, December 12, 1939," *Congressional Record*, February 23, 1940. Ogg clipped this *Congressional Record* and sent the relevant part to O'Neal. There is an arrow in red pencil pointing to Thatcher's statement.

[39] It was not until the period 1943-45, however, that the battle over the F.S.A. reached its climax.

In explaining the closer relations between the Department of Agriculture and the National Farmers' Union, former officials of the Administration stressed the point that the Farmers' Union was helping the Department to carry out programs which it wished to promote, such as co-operative marketing. Furthermore, from the standpoint of the power complex, the Department of Agriculture preferred to have three or four farm organizations to deal with rather than only one (the Farm Bureau).

The alignment of the Farmers' Union with organized labor, at a time when the harmonious relationship between the Farm Bureau and urban labor was breaking up, increased the rivalry between the two farm organizations. That there was a special link between the Farmers' Union and organized labor was, of course, a fact not denied but rather proclaimed by both. A public statement of a sympathetic understanding between the Farmers' Union and the Congress of Industrial Organizations was made on November 18, 1941, in a broadcast on a two-way radio hookup with James G. Patton, President of the Farmers' Union, speaking from the Farmers' Union convention at Topeka, Kansas, and James B. Carey, Secretary of the C.I.O., speaking from the C.I.O. convention in Detroit. As the Farm Bureau moved away from close relationships with both the Administration and with urban labor, the Farmers' Union appeared to be more than willing to fill the vacuum.[40]

An instance of the vital role of personalities in explaining the origin of some conflicts is to be found in the reorganization of the Farm Credit Administration in 1939. "The Farm Credit fight," as it was generally called in the Farm Bureau papers, brought on the open break between the Midwestern Farm Bureau leaders and the

[40] A few years later a belief was expressed among the "Big Four" farm organizations that a conspiracy existed between the U.S. Department of Agriculture, the Farmers' Union, and organized labor, to use the F.S.A. to build up the Farmers' Union and to weaken the influence of the Big Four. This charge was made by C. C. Teague, President of the National Council of Farmer Co-operatives, and circulated by him in a letter to the leaders of the other Big Four organizations (Teague to Ezra T. Benson, Executive Secretary of the National Council of Farmer Co-operatives, Albert S. Goss, Master of the National Grange, Edward A. O'Neal, President of the A.F.B.F., Charles W. Holman, Secretary of the National Co-operative Milk Producers' Federation, and Howard E. Babcock, Santa Paula, California, February 5, 1943, A.F.B.F., O'Neal Papers, carbon copy, but signed in ink). O'Neal's agreement with Teague's charges was more than perfunctory: "Our difficulty is that most of our farmers don't really realize the seriousness of this alignment of organized labor with the Farmers' Union and the Administration. They better wake up, and I am glad to see you feel the same way about it." O'Neal to Teague, February 23, 1943.

Roosevelt administration. In the first place, the principle of centralization of power was followed when President Roosevelt, in the spring of 1939, ordered the transfer of the Farm Credit Administration to the Department of Agriculture. It had previously been an independent agency. The Farm Bureau was in general opposed to centralization of power, but withheld opposition in this instance in the hope that Wallace would bring in "an outstanding man" (i.e., a sympathetic administrator), as governor. Certain farm bureaus were hopeful too that, under the new setup, credit facilities might be broadened. In particular there were complaints from the New England and California farm bureaus that many of their farmer members were too poor to obtain credit from the Farm Credit Administration, and too prosperous to obtain it from the F.S.A. O'Neal himself seemed not so much interested at that time in what Wallace might do with the Farm Credit Administration as in the possibility that the credit facilities of the F.S.A. might be extended to help the middle group of farmers not then being satisfactorily served by either of the major credit agencies.[41]

It was not until Wallace told O'Neal, confidentially, who the new governor was going to be that the fireworks began. Undoubtedly the man whom Wallace named to O'Neal was Dr. A. G. Black. O'Neal then warned Wallace of what Wallace must have known already—that the Midwestern farm bureaus would be very hostile to this choice.[42]

Dr. A. G. Black had been *persona non grata* to the Midwestern farm bureaus ever since the days when, as administrator of the corn-hog section of the A.A.A., he had been thought to be deliberately ignoring the Farm Bureau people in the naming of A.A.A. committeemen. The appointment of Black therefore appeared to be confirmation of what Farm Bureau leaders had suspected for several years, namely, that the Department of Agriculture was determined to ignore them in the making of agricultural policy. If the Farm Bureau was to function as a policy-making organization for agriculture, it had to be able not only to get the laws passed, but it had to be able also to influence the administrators. Midwestern farm bureaus had reasons for believing that they would not be able to influence Black.

[41] Telephone conversation between Wallace and O'Neal, November 16, 1939, A.F.B.F., O'Neal Papers (typescript); and memorandum of telephone conversation between Earl Smith and O'Neal, November 17, 1939, *ibid.*
[42] Telephone conversation between Wallace and O'Neal, November 17, 1939, *ibid.*

When Wallace not only recommended the appointment of Black as governor of the Farm Credit Administration, but subsequently supported a bill to increase the powers of the governor over farm credit, the Farm Bureau became aroused on the issue of decentralization of power as well.

The fact that Wallace went out to a National Farmers' Union meeting at St. Paul, Minnesota, on April 27, 1940, to explain and defend his views on the farm credit situation did nothing to reassure the Farm Bureau. Henceforth, interfarm organization rivalries became an important element in the controversy over farm credit. Numerous confidential letters from Midwestern Farm Bureau leaders to O'Neal expressed the belief that the agencies of the Department of Agriculture in the Midwest, particularly the A.A.A., were being used to promote attendance at the Farmers' Union meeting in St. Paul.[43]

Another case, apart from that of the Farm Credit Administration, in which the personality of the administrator was important in precipitating conflict, was that of the F.S.A. The intense hostility of the Farm Bureau to the F.S.A. was not aroused until C. B. Baldwin became administrator. His predecessor, Dr. Will Alexander, had preferred to compromise on the best program he could get rather than to bring conflict into the open. O'Neal could work with him. But he could not work with Baldwin, who seemed to prefer an open fight to a compromise.

The archetype of the administrator whom farmers of the Farm Bureau sort could neither understand nor like was Rex Tugwell. Tugwell was an urban liberal, which was quite a different species from an agrarian liberal. As another agricultural statesman has said, he had a lovely free spirit, but farmers were alternately bewildered, amused, and enraged by some of the frills that his agencies sponsored—frills such as the "special skills" program, encouragement of folk-singing, and the like. Besides, Tugwell apparently took a positive delight in insulting people of the Farm Bureau–Extension Service sort. This personality clash was just an added irritant to the basic clash over the nature of the farm program.

For his part, Tugwell viewed the Farm Bureau as "the most sinister influence in America." From the first, he warned Henry A. Wallace about Farm Bureau people. Nonetheless Wallace worked

---

[43] A.F.B.F., O'Neal Papers.

with them in the beginning. Finally the Farm Bureau cut Wallace's throat, said Tugwell.[44]

The influence of personalities in farm organization politics was also significant. When John Simpson, who had been president of the Farmers' Union at the opening of the New Deal period, was replaced by James G. Patton as president, with M. W. Thatcher as the power behind the throne, the Roosevelt administration found the new Farmers' Union leadership much more congenial to work with. This was particularly true of Thatcher.

The part played by partisan political considerations in explaining conflicts among agricultural forces is everywhere suggested and nowhere easy to grasp. Farm Bureau officials believed that an important reason for the attempts of the Department of Agriculture to centralize control over the administration of action programs, thus reducing the authority and influence of the land-grant colleges and Extension Services, was a political one. This arose from the fact that Extension officials in some Northeastern and Midwestern states were likely to be Republican or to be controlled by state administrations which were Republican. They were presumed therefore to be nuclei of Republican influence, which the Administration naturally had no wish to strengthen. Since farm policy was a bipartisan product according to the Farm Bureau creed, it did not matter whether Extension officials administering the New Deal farm program were Republican or not.

The heart of the conflict between the Farm Bureau and the Department of Agriculture was reached in the contest over the county land-use planning committees. The basic issue was: How should farm policy be made, and by whom? Of course it was granted that Congress had the final voice and the final decision-making power in agricultural legislation, along with the President. But farm policy-making had not normally originated with Congress, at least not in recent times.

Through the county land-use planning system, the Department of Agriculture sought to solve many of the problems of relationships between agencies with which it was plagued; and at the same time to take democratic planning of programs down to the "grass roots." Actually there was far more to the system than the county committees, but these were considered the heart of it, and it was usually designated as county land-use planning. There is no doubt that the initiative for the scheme came from the Department of Agriculture,

---

[44] Tugwell, personal interview, November 29, 1949.

but it was put into operation following the Mount Weather Agreement made in 1938 between a committee representing the Department of Agriculture and a committee representing the Association of Land-Grant Colleges and Universities.[45]

A basic assumption of those who originated the land-use planning program was that "the trend toward strong central governments . . . is universal and inevitable."[46] The problem, as they saw it, was how to keep both policy-making and administration democratic. The answer, they believed, lay in farmer participation in the democratic process.

The essential framework for the land-use planning program consisted of a state committee in each state, a county committee in each agricultural county, and some community committees as well. The state committee consisted of a representative of each of the action agencies in the Department of Agriculture (such as the A.A.A. and the F.S.A.), the state director of Extension (as chairman), the director of the state experiment station, representatives of any other state agencies having responsibility for land-use programs, and a number of representative farm men and women.

The county committees were considered more important from the standpoint of democratic planning in agriculture. The county agent of the Extension Service was the secretary of the county committee, which consisted of 10 to 20 farm men and women (democratically elected), as well as the county representatives of the agricultural action agencies. The farmer membership on the county committee was supposed always to be in the majority. The community committees, consisting of farm men and women, were expected to help the county committees.

The purely administrative work involved in the various action programs was carried out by the agencies of the Department, though the state committee was expected to assist in such matters as adjudication of conflicts. The Department's really great expectations of the county land-use planning program lay in the realm of policy formulation. The Department hoped, through the land-use planning committees, to reach directly down to the grass roots, and tap great reservoirs of ideas among the farmers themselves at the local level. M. L. Wilson, who more than anyone else was probably

---

[45] For a brief and clear statement of how the county land-use planning program originated, see Bushrod W. Allin, "County Planning Project—a Co-operative Approach to Agricultural Planning," *Journal of Farm Economics*, XXII (February, 1940), 292-301.

[46] *Ibid.*

the philosophical father of the plan, spoke of the need, in a world threatened by totalitarianism, "to battle for a renaissance of democracy and for new democratic patterns in farm life and the rural community."[47] Echoing John Dewey, he maintained, "The best way to save democracy is to use it."[48]

It soon became clear to the Department of Agriculture "that the Department itself was in need of a central planning agency through which local people could make themselves heard."[49] To meet this need, the Bureau of Agricultural Economics was reorganized and given the responsibility for the general planning work of the Department.[50]

No more unfortunate term or concept could have been employed than that of "a central planning agency." To Farm Bureau leaders this sounded more like bureaucracy than democracy. Additionally, they believed that the whole system of state and county committees was designed to reduce the Extension Service to a minor role and to bypass the Farm Bureau altogether. Instead of being chief among agricultural agencies on the state and local level, the Extension Service would be only *primus inter pares,* and perhaps not even *primus,* if the other agencies chose to combine against it.

It was part of the Farm Bureau creed that national policy for agriculture should be formulated by independent national farm organizations (i.e., the A.F.B.F.). It was frequently reiterated in Farm Bureau circles that farmers should speak through their own independent organizations, rather than through government organizations, even if these were designated "co-operative."

In Departmental thinking, however, the Farm Bureau was not an independent organization on account of its special relationship with the Extension Service. And further, it was alleged that farm policy as produced by the A.F.B.F. was more a product of its resolutions committee, over which Earl Smith presided, than it was of farmers at the grass roots.

In any case, a nationwide system of farmer committees always contained potentialities, in the eyes of the leaders of the A.F.B.F., that it might develop into a powerful rival farm organization. Earl

---

[47] M. L. Wilson, "Facets of County Planning: On Using Democracy," *Land Policy Review,* II (January-February, 1939), 1-4.

[48] *Ibid.*

[49] U.S. Department of Agriculture, *Land Use Planning Under Way, July, 1940* (a booklet prepared by the Bureau of Agricultural Economics in co-operation with other agencies), p. 4.

[50] *Ibid.*

Smith had always been especially wary of farmer committees for this reason.

The county land-use planning program was buried in the early 1940's,[51] and there is no doubt that the A.F.B.F. was the chief undertaker. By 1940 the Farm Bureau had already demonstrated two parts of its strategy. One was to make sure that Farm Bureau members were elected to the county land-use planning committees. This was easy in the states in which the Farm Bureau was the most powerful farm organization.[52] The other was to come out with a sweeping plan of its own for the co-ordination of the administration of government programs. The third and most effective part of the strategy was held in reserve until 1941, when the A.F.B.F. began to use its influence in Congress to reduce appropriations for the offending agencies.[53] The A.F.B.F. was not wholly responsible for the burial of county land-use planning, for there were inherent weaknesses in the system, as Gross has pointed out. One was that instead of the spontaneous democracy that was assumed to exist among farmers at the local level, there was apathy against which special efforts should have been made to arouse a desire for self-help. The other was that the system *was* far too heavily weighted on the side of bureaucracy, with one in every four members of committees a government employee.[54] There was the further fact that involvement in World War II turned major attention to other matters.

The Farm Bureau's master plan to counter the Department's efforts at co-ordination and county planning was contained in a "Resolution for the Co-ordination of Agricultural Agencies" adopted at the annual meeting of the A.F.B.F. in December, 1940.[55] This resolution began by deploring the "duplication and overlapping" of the various agricultural agencies. ("Duplication" and "overlapping" soon became favorite Farm Bureau phrases.) In order to bring

[51] Neal C. Gross, "A Post-Mortem on County Planning," *Journal of Farm Economics,* XXV (August, 1943), 644-61, analyzes the reason for the demise. An earlier article that gives a critical analysis of county land-use planning while it was still functioning is J. G. Crawford and Gunnar Lange, "County Planning for Land-Use Adjustment," *ibid.,* XXII (May, 1940), 473-92.

[52] Gross, *op. cit.*

[53] Hardin, "The Bureau of Agricultural Economics Under Fire: A Study in Valuation Conflicts," pp. 635-68, analyzes this strategy, carried on between 1941 and 1946, which resulted in the death of the state and county land-use planning program in 1942, and the attrition of the Bureau of Agricultural Economics. O'Neal's goal was that the B.A.E. should be confined to statistical and fact-finding research.

[54] Gross, *op. cit.*

[55] A.F.B.F., *Resolutions of the Annual Meeting,* 1940.

about co-ordination, it recommended sweeping changes in the administration of the national agricultural programs.

Two main areas of change were proposed. (1) On the national level a five-man, nonpartisan board should be set up within the Department of Agriculture to administer the A.A.A., the Soil Conservation Service, and other similar agencies, as well as the planning activities of the Bureau of Agricultural Economics. "This board should be representative of the nation's agriculture." Furthermore, "it should be independent in its position with respect to other bureaus and agencies of government." (2) In the field of state and local administration, the gist of the recommendation was that most of the programs should be turned over to the Extension Service. For some of those regulatory and other functions which the Extension Service was known to be very wary of accepting, other arrangements were to be made, but even in such cases the Extension director would nominate the persons to compose the state committee, after consultation with statewide farm organizations.[56]

If this appears to be a plan to place all of the national programs for agriculture under the Extension Service, it was only superficially so. The fundamental aim was to take control of agricultural programs away from the Department of Agriculture, which was believed to be no longer the farmers' advocate, and give it to the farmers themselves (i.e., the organized farmers). We have O'Neal's word for this.

In a letter to Walter Hammond, a fellow Farm Bureau leader, O'Neal explained that the object of the resolution was that farmers should take charge of the agricultural programs. Where farmers were well organized, O'Neal argued, whether in the Farm Bureau, the Grange, or the Farmers' Union, then the Extension Service did as farmers wished. Further, he continued:

It is up to the farmers to assert themselves in an organized way. If a County Agent does not deliver, it is up to the farmers to get rid of him. If a Director of Extension does not deliver, let the farmers get rid of him. . . . I tell you, Walter, the time has passed when farmers can get anything without fighting for it; and the time is past when they can expect a farm program to be run in their interest unless they take charge of it. That is the whole aim and purpose of our program as outlined in our Resolution on co-ordination of Administration of the action agencies. . . .[57]

The A.F.B.F.'s resolution on co-ordination was never adopted by the government.

---

[56] *Ibid.*

[57] O'Neal to Hammond, President of the Texas Farm Bureau, April 10, 1941.

CHAPTER XI

The Election of 1940

The growing antagonism in 1940 between the Midwestern Farm Bureau leadership and the Roosevelt administration was further exacerbated by a series of events in connection with the political campaign of 1940.

One of these was the A.A.A. dinners held in various places throughout the Midwest on March 8, 1940, to commemorate the establishment of the A.A.A.[1] It would have been natural for the farm bureaus to take the lead, or at least to join in these celebrations, since the Farm Bureau itself maintained that the A.A.A. was the offspring of its own ideas adopted by the Roosevelt administration. Moreover, the Midwestern farm bureaus had vigorously supported the A.A.A. in its early days. Midwestern Farm Bureau leaders suspected, however, that the purpose of these dinners was not so much to commemorate the accomplishments of the A.A.A. as it was to win votes for the Democratic Party in the campaign. Under such circumstances, to have joined in the celebrations would have been a violation of the Farm Bureau doctrine that farm policy was a nonpartisan affair. They therefore voted not to participate in the dinners.[2] Since most of the Midwestern Farm Bureau leaders were Republican by tradition, they were particularly zealous guardians, during the Democratic administrations, of the creed of nonpartisanship in farm policy.

---

[1] The date chosen was the anniversary of the day (March 8, 1933) when President Roosevelt directed Henry A. Wallace to call a conference of representative farmers and farm leaders to discuss legislation for a national farm program. Radio speech by Wallace, March 8, 1940 (press release).

[2] "Minutes of the Midwest Presidents' and Secretaries' Conference, Des Moines, Iowa, February 21, 1940," A.F.B.F. files, folder marked "Midwest Conferences, 1940."

During the campaign of 1940, Henry A. Wallace publicly challenged the most sacred of all Farm Bureau beliefs—that the New Deal for agriculture was a nonpartisan accomplishment made possible by sectional co-operation between Midwest and South. In a campaign speech at Topeka, Kansas (the scene of Franklin D. Roosevelt's famous campaign speech on farm policy in 1932), Wallace cited the record to show that all the major New Deal acts in aid of agriculture had been opposed by a majority of the Republican members in Congress. The Republican record of unfriendliness to farmers had continued after 1932, said Wallace. He then cited the following statistics of party votes. In 1933, 62 per cent of the Republicans in Congress voted *against* the A.A.A. In 1936, 75 per cent of them voted against the Soil Conservation and Domestic Allotment Act. In 1938, 85 per cent of them voted against the second A.A.A. In 1939, 82 per cent of them voted against parity payments. And in 1940, 82 per cent of them voted against parity payments, "just to show how consistent" they were.[3]

The logical inference from this speech was that the New Deal for agriculture was an achievement not of bipartisan (or of nonpartisan) policy, but of the Democratic Party. Whereas O'Neal and the Farm Bureau were accustomed to keeping tabulations of sectional voting records in Congress, Wallace clearly implied that it was only party voting records that mattered.

"It is going to be hard to hold the cornbelt states in the Democratic column," wrote O'Neal in August of 1940.[4] The elections of November confirmed this prediction.

Why Roosevelt lost the Midwest in 1940 has been the subject of various interpretations. As only one of these, the Farm Bureau explanation does not provide the complete answer, but it does contribute to it.

Roosevelt himself appears to have sought an explanation from O'Neal. A brief letter, signed only with the typewritten initials F. D. R., and on stationery bearing a White House letterhead, is among the O'Neal manuscripts.[5] It reads, in full:

MEMORANDUM FOR ED O'NEAL:
(Personal and Confidential)
I have only just seen a copy of the Illinois Agricultural Association Record for November 1940 (Volume 18 Number 11) in which the leading article "This Month" was written by Earl Smith.

[3] Extracts from Wallace's speech at Topeka, Kansas, quoted in *Wallace's Farmer*, October 19, 1940.
[4] O'Neal to L. N. Duncan, August 29, 1940.
[5] Roosevelt to O'Neal, January 9, 1941.

Frankly, I am a bit surprised. I had previously thought that Earl Smith was at least non-partisan. Some day perhaps you will give me your personal slant, in confidence.

F. D. R.

Another letter, which is in the same envelope as this note, is signed with the typewritten initials C. C. D. (undoubtedly Chester C. Davis). Davis said that he was returning F. D. R.'s note as O'Neal had asked, and he described a talk which he had had with the President on November 9 about the elections in the agricultural states, in which the President had mentioned Earl Smith's name. After assuring Roosevelt that Earl Smith had been "in our corner" in 1932 and 1936, Chester Davis stated that he believed that Earl Smith's article in the November *Illinois Agricultural Association Record* "was clearly open to the inference that the writer was not supporting the President." The interpretation which Davis gave the President for the defection of Earl Smith and other Midwestern farm leaders in 1940 was:

I stated that Earl, and other midwestern farm leaders who may have left us in this Campaign, could have been kept in camp if the Department of Agriculture had continued to treat them as consultants and friends. I gave my impression that for nearly two years the men in the Department had ceased to consult the Farm Bureau, the Co-operatives, or the Grange, on important matters, and that they had elevated Thatcher[6] into a position of Chief Adviser for organized agriculture. Under the circumstances it was not surprising to me that some of the farm leaders had become lukewarm, even hostile. I urged him to get back on the basis where all the farm leaders were consulted and given the consideration merited by the interests they represented.[7]

President Roosevelt seems to have leaned toward "the German vote explanation" (which is, probably, that hostility among the German ethnic groups in the Midwest to his foreign policy with respect to the European war led them to vote against him). Davis' letter continued: "It was during this conversation that the President gave me the 'German vote' explanation of the results in the farm states which he had received from Thatcher, whom he had seen just before my appointment. I told him that, in my judgment, there was much more to the matter than that."[8]

Earl Smith's article,[9] referred to by "F. D. R." and "C. C. D.,"

---

[6] Thatcher was then the legislative representative in Washington for the Farmers' Union, and head of the Farmers' Union Grain Terminal Association.

[7] C. C. D. to O'Neal, January 28, 1941.

[8] *Ibid.*

[9] Earl C. Smith, "This Month," *Illinois Agricultural Association Record*, November, 1940, pp. 3-4.

gave a succinct and clear statement of the nonpartisan policy which had been followed by farm organizations since the 1920's—that is, the doctrine that farmers should vote as farmers, not as party members. Then Smith advised what seems to be a break with this traditional policy, by declaring that in the election of 1940 farmers should not place paramount emphasis on agricultural policy but instead on other campaign issues. This actually was not a break with the old policy but was a continuation of it under new circumstances. For the first time in recent history, so Earl Smith believed, the two major parties were in fundamental agreement on agricultural policy. The following two paragraphs represent the heart of Earl Smith's statement:

During election campaigns since the middle 1920s, farm organizations have been urging farm people to consider first and foremost the needs of agriculture, and to present a solid front in support of candidates, regardless of party affiliation, whose position and commitments were most satisfactory in support of fundamental principles of law necessary to the solution of the farm problem.

During the present campaign, however, farm organizations are not justified in urging farm people to be guided wholly by statements of candidates on agricultural issues. This is true not because the agricultural problem is any less important, but rather because party commitments and expressions by leading candidates are in general agreement as to the importance of solving the farm problem and ultimate objectives to be sought through any farm policy or program, although not altogether in agreement as to method of applying fundamental law or laws.[10]

In support of his statement, Smith cited the agricultural planks of both the Republican and the Democratic party platforms in the campaign of 1940, and, more significantly, quoted statements by candidates. For the Democratic point of view he quoted, perhaps with malice aforethought, not President Roosevelt's but Secretary Wallace's assurances that the existing farm program would be continued. Smith's emphasis is, however, on quotations from the Republican Presidential candidate, Wendell Willkie. Such emphasis should not be interpreted as necessarily implying that Smith favored Willkie, but only that Willkie's position on farm policy required elaboration because it was less well known than that of the man who had been President for two terms. Wallace's assurance that the existing farm program would be continued was matched by Willkie's statement: "I do not favor changing the present farm program unless a better one is gradually evolved."[11] Two further quotations

[10] *Ibid.*
[11] *Ibid.*

indicate that Willkie was particularly angling for the Midwestern farm vote. In his acceptance speech at Elwood, Indiana, Willkie said: "I believe that the federal government has a responsibility to equalize the lot of the farmer with that of the manufacturer. If this cannot be done through parity of prices, other means must be found with the least possible regimentation of the farmer's affairs."[12] Later, at Omaha,Willkie declared that the national farm policy *is* established. "It is not a partisan issue."[13]

When Willkie's statements are assessed against the history of Midwestern agricultural politics, their shrewd appeal is obvious. It was in the Midwest that the slogan "Equality for Agriculture" was born in pre–McNary-Haugen days. By 1940 Midwestern farmers were generally still faithful to the concept of equality as embodied in the New Deal goal of "parity," but were showing definite signs of restlessness with the means used in the New Deal to achieve that goal, namely, production control or, more slurringly, "regimentation." That farm policy should be nonpartisan had been a principle far more cherished in the Midwest than it ever had been among the firmly Republican farmers of the Northeast or the devoted Democrats of the South.

Since there was little difference between the two major candidates on farm policy, it was other issues, Smith implied, that should be decisive. Among the other issues to which he called the attention of farmers was: "The ultimate effect upon our form of government through establishing the precedent of a third term for the President."[14] It was thus made clear that Earl Smith was opposed to the election of Roosevelt for a third term.

The obvious sectional split within agriculture in 1940 was a source of grave concern to O'Neal, who was still a staunch Democrat and still a supporter of the Roosevelt administration. That O'Neal privately believed the unity in agriculture between the Midwest and the South in 1932 and 1936 had been not a nonpartisan affair but a Democratic Party achievement was certainly implied by him in a letter to Roosevelt.[15] In this letter, written shortly after the elections of November, 1940, O'Neal expressed his fear that agriculture faced a new crisis because the unity between the Midwestern and Southern agrarian regions in support of the Roosevelt administration and its farm program had been broken. In 1940 the

[12] *Ibid.*
[13] *Ibid.*
[14] *Ibid.*
[15] O'Neal to Roosevelt, November 30, 1940.

Southern and border states had remained loyal to the Democratic administration, but O'Neal conceded that a majority of farmers in the Midwest had gone over to the Republican Party. O'Neal's primary object was to restore unity in agriculture, and concerning this he told President Roosevelt: "Unity for agriculture must mean, under present circumstances, support for your administration and its farm program."[16]

The crisis was one not only for agriculture but for the Democratic Party, O'Neal believed. Unless the united support of both the major agricultural sections—Midwest and South—could be achieved once again, he warned President Roosevelt that the Democratic Party would become solely "the party of the South and of the great industrial centers, in accordance with the last election returns."[17]

To mend the split—that is, to bring back the support of Midwestern agriculture to the Democratic administration—O'Neal advised the President to replace the incumbent Secretary of Agriculture. Without disparaging Claude Wickard (who had become Secretary when Wallace resigned to run for Vice-President, and whose appointment O'Neal had himself endorsed at that time), O'Neal pleaded that the times called not simply for a good Secretary like Wickard, but for a great one. The one man, so O'Neal believed, who had the supreme confidence of farmers in all sections and in all farm organizations—the man who could be a great Secretary—was Chester Davis.[18]

O'Neal's suggestion as to how the split in agriculture might best be mended was based on the assumption that the primary cause of the division was in the relationship between the Department of Agriculture and Midwestern farmers. In a conversation with the President in 1941, O'Neal apparently made explicit his interpretation of why the Midwest had swung away from Roosevelt in 1940.[19] Bluntly stated, it was because Wallace had antagonized Midwestern farmers. Among the errors of Wallace enumerated by O'Neal were

---

[16] *Ibid.*

[17] *Ibid.*

[18] *Ibid.* The President, whom O'Neal had once considered his promising pupil in agricultural politics, gave no sign that he had received this advice. Later Roosevelt, who by now was certainly no amateur in agricultural politics himself, appointed Davis to the post of War Food Administrator, a position which might be considered of greater importance than that of Secretary of Agriculture.

[19] Memorandum made by O'Neal after talking with the President, January 31, 1941, A.F.B.F., O'Neal Papers.

"his desertion of the Farm Bureau since 1937" and "his political actions."[20]

On subsequent occasions, O'Neal returned to the same theme repeatedly. For instance, there was his plaint to Bernard Baruch about Roosevelt: "If he had listened. In 1940 I told him if Henry Wallace took charge of the Democratic campaign in the Midwest we would lose it. They didn't listen to me."[21]

Other interpretations of the Midwestern farm vote will be mentioned here, to give perspective to the Farm Bureau interpretation. One was that by 1940 Midwestern farmers were too prosperous to vote for a continuation of the New Deal, and the old pattern was re-established—that is, a prosperous Midwestern farmer votes Republican. Another, applying to the four northern Great Plains states only, was that farmers in this region were still so poor after seven years of the New Deal that their Republican vote was a protest vote. It may be that both these explanations, incongruous as they appear, are valid. The New Deal farm program had been primarily based on the goal of security. Having achieved security, Midwestern farmers were ready to put more emphasis on the goals of freedom and economic progress. In the Great Plains states, a succession of serious droughts occurred within the seven years of the New Deal. Consequently New Deal success in raising the prices of farm products meant little to a region where the vagaries of the weather had caused production to be so low that there was little income from crops at any price. Having failed therefore to achieve security under the New Deal farm program, the northern Great Plains states were ready to protest against it by voting Republican.[22] Thus

---

[20] *Ibid.*

[21] Telephone conversation between O'Neal and Baruch, June 26, 1942, A.F.B.F., O'Neal Papers (typescript).

[22] The "protest vote" theory is only a partial explanation, however, of the Republican vote in the Great Plains. A lucid statement of this theory as well as of two others is given by a South Dakota editor to whom O'Neal wrote asking for such information (W. R. Ronald to O'Neal, November 21, 1940). According to Ronald there was some support for the "German vote" theory, since the parts of South Dakota where a high percentage of the people are of German descent did vote for Willkie. Additionally, however, he pointed out that neither the German nor the protest vote theories explained the heavily Republican vote in eastern South Dakota, where crops had been good and where the farm population was Scandinavian rather than German. Here he believed that the failure of the New Deal to achieve its goal of parity and speeches of Republican candidates were quite influential. He mentioned specifically Wendell Willkie's promise to continue the existing farm program while trying to find something better. These relatively prosperous farmers, after waiting so long in vain for the New Deal promise of parity prices to be

frustration in the northern Great Plains and complacency in the corn belt may have brought forth the same swing in voting behavior.

In the later part of the New Deal period, a shifting alignment of forces helps to explain much of the conflict that occurred. New relationships among interest groups, and between them and the Administration, were forming. The new alignment placed organized labor with the Administration on the one side, and most of organized agriculture along with business on the other. In time of depression, the A.F.B.F. had found its best ally in urban labor. As prosperity returned, and as farmers no longer found themselves so dependent on the support of the representatives of urban labor to gain Congressional appropriations, the Farm Bureau leaders tended to align themselves more with the forces of organized business.

During the early New Deal period, the common enemy in Congress of both labor and agriculture had been the "economy bloc." As late as 1937 O'Neal characterized both the senators from Virginia as reactionary.[23] But by the early 1940's the A.F.B.F. had become one of the strongest supporters of Senator Byrd of Virginia, spearhead of the drive for economy, in his activities as chairman of the Joint Committee on the Reduction of Non-Essential Federal Expenditures. In this case the chief target of both Senator Byrd's committee and of the A.F.B.F. was the F.S.A. O'Neal's frank recognition of the shifting relationships among labor, agriculture, and business is stated in a letter from him to the editor of *Fortune:* "Frankly, you know also that labor has, in the last few years come along in a fine fashion with our farm organization group to a greater degree than have the industrialists. A number of the industrialists, however, are now having a much broader vision of the farm problem."[24]

The Farm Bureau leaders were by then greatly disturbed over what they believed to be the attitude of the Roosevelt administration. "It looks to us as if our government is largely turned over to organized labor," declared O'Neal.[25]

While the year 1940 marks a turning point in the relationship between the A.F.B.F. and the Roosevelt administration, there was

---

fulfilled, felt that they had everything to gain and nothing to lose by voting for Willkie.

[23] "Your Virginia Senators are both reactionary," wrote O'Neal to G. F. Holsinger, President of the Virginia Farm Bureau, February 15, 1937.

[24] O'Neal to Raymond Leslie Buell, August 29, 1941.

[25] *Ibid.*

by no means a break between them on all issues and in all sections. It was in 1940, for example, that the A.F.B.F. gave strong and perhaps indispensable support to Roosevelt and to Secretary of State Cordell Hull in the struggle for the renewal of the reciprocal trade program. Likewise, the antitrust division of the Department of Justice, under Thurman Arnold, found farmers generally more interested in its antimonopoly crusade than was urban labor. Arnold therefore looked to the Farm Bureau for support, which was unhesitatingly given.

Farm Bureau support for the antitrust campaign of the Department of Justice was not confined to good wishes, but was applied where it counted most—that is, to Congressional appropriations. When Arnold wrote to O'Neal, early in 1940, of his distress because the House appropriation would require him to cut his staff to 25 men,[26] O'Neal immediately wrote to several influential senators, urging them to support the restoration of the proposed cut for the Department of Justice, and to provide additional funds for the proper enforcement of the antitrust laws.[27] By May, 1941, a Farm Bureau spokesman was rejoicing over a great victory in the Senate for antitrust appropriations.[28] Whether or not the A.F.B.F. had led this fight, as he maintained, it is indisputable that the Farm Bureau had warmly supported it. Thus, in spite of shifting alignments the A.F.B.F. remained a separate force to be reckoned with in controversies over national policy.

[26] Arnold to O'Neal, February 9, 1940.

[27] O'Neal to Senator John H. Bankhead, February 19, 1940; O'Neal to Senator Kenneth McKellar, February 19, 1940.

[28] W. R. Ogg to O'Neal, May 19, 1941. See also *Congressional Record*, May 19, 1941.

CHAPTER XII

Conclusion

A review of the actual policies favored by the Farm Bureau during the New Deal period indicates that the basic type of economic policy in which the A.F.B.F. was interested was price policy. While O'Neal was eager to have the advice of expert economists, his own concept of the aim of price policy was not formulated in terms of sophisticated economic theory. It was simply to raise the price of farm products. This he felt to be morally just, since farm prices had been depressed lower and longer than had other prices or wages. He was not the originator, but he became a leading apostle of parity as the yardstick by which the level of farm product prices was to be measured—the goal being to restore and maintain the relationship between farm prices and other prices that had existed in the golden age of agriculture, 1909-14.

During the early days of the New Deal, Midwestern Farm Bureau members were as eager as the Southern members to see the disastrously low farm prices raised through action by the federal government. By 1940, with farm prices considerably higher but with parity still not achieved, Southern Farm Bureau leaders wished to press on for parity. Midwesterners, however, were beginning to question the wisdom of such a policy, since it was well understood that governmental support of prices inevitably was accompanied by governmental controls, and the greater the support, probably the greater the control. A threatened split between the Southern and the Midwestern farm bureaus over the issue of the level of price supports was averted in 1940 by a compromise resolution, adopted at the annual general meeting of the A.F.B.F., according to the terms of which 85 per cent of parity was endorsed as the desirable level.

Almost immediately, attempts were made to raise prices above this level. It is probable that the initiative for attacks on the compromise level of support prices (at 85 per cent of parity) came not from within the Farm Bureau but from within Congress. Even before the Farm Bureau's compromise resolution was adopted, certain Southern members of Congress had been advocating mandatory commodity loans (or some combination of commodity loans plus direct payments) which would guarantee to farmers prices at 100 per cent of parity. For instance, in April, 1940, Congressman Cannon informed O'Neal that he was for 100 per cent of parity, and further added: "We are in a good position because it is coming up first and the same food boys will have to vote for us before we vote for them."[1] Congressman Pace was another who was reported to be dissatisfied with anything less than 100 per cent of parity.[2] Within the Farm Bureau, below the surface, tension continued to mount over the issue of price policy.[3]

Price policy, however, was not the only theme upon which the Farm Bureau relied, though it was the theme to which the Farm Bureau gave most attention during the New Deal period. In terms of economic policy, from time to time the Farm Bureau had sought the solution to farm problems through monetary and fiscal policy, tariff policy, and antimonopoly measures. These were all means within the agrarian tradition to which the Farm Bureau might turn again with renewed emphasis, particularly if there were dissension within the Farm Bureau over price policy.

[1] Telephone conversation between Cannon and O'Neal, April 24, 1940, A.F.B.F., O'Neal Papers (typescript). Cannon was obviously declaring that farm congressmen would not vote funds for the relief of the urban unemployed unless urban congressmen voted in favor of funds to support farm product prices at parity levels.

[2] W. R. Ogg informed O'Neal of Pace's position. Telephone conversation between O'Neal, Ogg, and Walter Randolph, November 7, 1941, *ibid.*

[3] The intraorganizational struggle became an open one in 1943, when Earl Smith clashed with the Southern Farm Bureau contingents over the determination of parity itself. When the A.F.B.F. executive committee, with strong Southern support and under O'Neal's leadership, endorsed the Pace bill to include the wages of farm labor in the parity index, Earl Smith asked to be recorded as voting "no." This exceptional procedure (for the votes of the executive committee were seldom recorded) doubtless indicates Earl Smith's strong convictions on the subject. It was Smith's view that the inclusion of the wages of farm labor would turn the parity index into a "cost of production" concept. The minutes of the committee record that Mr. Smith stated that he would not fight the bill, but felt obligated to convey the views of the Illinois Agricultural Association to the Illinois congressmen. A.F.B.F., "Minutes of the Executive Committee," *Minutes of the Board of Directors,* January 31–February 2, 1943.

Through its monetary policy, the Farm Bureau carried on the tradition of the earlier farm protest movements which had sought to arouse interest in the general price level as a means of alleviating farm distress. (The policy of "parity," in contrast, was concerned with relative price levels as between agricultural and other commodities.) The emphasis of the Farm Bureau during the New Deal period was not, however, on monetary policy as the chief instrument by which the farm problem was to be solved, but on such measures as the Agricultural Adjustment Act, by which it was hoped that parity prices would be achieved. Again and again the Northeastern farm bureaus, to whom the monetary program was paramount, complained that the A.F.B.F. was neglecting monetary policy in favor of the policies of the A.A.A. To these complaints President O'Neal always indignantly replied with a full, though rather unconvincing, account of the efforts that he and the Washington staff had made on behalf of the Northeast's monetary program, which involved the goal of the "commodity dollar." In any case, the A.F.B.F. was happy to use its political pressure to aid Roosevelt in securing Congressional enactment of the New Deal monetary program.

In fiscal policy too, the A.F.B.F. followed the lead of the earlier agrarian reformers. From the early 1920's the progressive income tax was the chief plank in its fiscal platform, and the basic principle was stated that taxation should tend to produce a more equitable distribution of wealth.[4] Efforts to reduce federal income taxes in 1923, allegedly inspired by Andrew Mellon's attempts to free his fellow wealthy industrialists of part of their tax burden, were roundly condemned by the A.F.B.F., as were similar efforts to lower corporation taxes in 1926.

From the early 1930's, the A.F.B.F. recognized the principles eventually embodied in the New Deal—that the costs of government could not be reduced to former levels, and that efforts should therefore be directed to securing "equitable" types of taxes. Though equitable taxes to the Farm Bureau seemed to mean those which lessen, or at least prevent, the increase of the burden of taxation on land and other general property, nevertheless the emphasis on the progressive income tax was in line with the New Deal taxation policies.

More important, however, than any specific measure was the Farm Bureau's general approach to the government's fiscal policy

---

[4] A.F.B.F., *Resolutions of the Annual Meeting*, 1921 and subsequent years.

that gradually evolved during the New Deal period—a policy that came to be associated with Keynesian ideas even if Lord Keynes himself would not have recognized them. The Farm Bureau's alignment in the mid-1930's with urban labor interest groups against those whom O'Neal called "the economy boys" probably facilitated the Roosevelt program of relief and recovery from depression through spending—a policy which the Roosevelt administration at first drifted into as an incidental outcome of other specific action, and only in the so-called second phase of the New Deal consciously recognized as a countercyclical device of primary importance. The *rapprochement* between the Farm Bureau and representatives of urban labor, while it lasted, was on the basis of a common general approach to fiscal policy, rather than on the basis of fundamental harmony on such specific demands as higher prices for farm products on the part of the one group, or higher wages for labor on the part of the other.

The A.F.B.F.'s record on foreign trade policy was not a consistent one. At one stage, during the 1920's, the A.F.B.F. under Midwestern dominance had hoped to find salvation from agricultural depression through raising the protective tariff especially on farm products. It was not until after the Hawley-Smoot tariff of 1930 that disillusionment with this policy was widespread. Even so, the Midwesterners were reluctant to abandon protectionism. Franklin Roosevelt's original reciprocal trade program probably owes nothing to the A.F.B.F. However, by 1940, as we have seen, O'Neal, who was a Southerner and a free trader by heredity and conviction, had won the support of the A.F.B.F., including Midwesterners, for the renewal of Roosevelt's reciprocal trade program. Nonetheless, an undercurrent of traditional Midwestern antipathy to economic internationalism remained. This was particularly true of the old-guard Midwestern leaders like Earl Smith, who, while intellectually convinced of the rationale of the reciprocal trade program, were still emotionally steeped in a culture in which "internationalism" was used as a condemnatory phrase.[5]

---

[5] Finally, in 1943, Earl Smith supported a motion which could only be interpreted as hostile to the reciprocal trade program. This was a motion to reserve to Congress, instead of the Administration, the right to exercise the "escape clause." With respect to this motion, Mr. Smith specifically asked that his vote be recorded, and accordingly a roll call is given in the *Minutes of the Board of Directors*, May 31–June 2, 1943. Since the vote was 5 yeas to 11 nays, the motion which Smith favored was lost, but it is significant to find three Midwestern states—Illinois, Iowa, and Indiana—lining up with the California Farm Bureau, which had always been bitterly hostile to the reciprocal trade

The Midwest was not a unit, however, on tariff or foreign trade policy. The Ohio Farm Bureau, under Perry Green and Murray Lincoln, was fervently internationalistic. In Iowa, Francis Johnson, President of the state Farm Bureau, represented the old-guard protectionist policy. Conversely, Allan Kline (in 1940 Vice-President of the Iowa Farm Bureau, soon to be its president, and subsequently to be O'Neal's successor as president of the A.F.B.F.) represented the other segment of Iowa thinking, which was liberally internationalistic. Such younger Midwestern leaders as Kline were closer to O'Neal in their thinking on tariff policy than they were to Earl Smith or Francis Johnson. (In price policy, however, most of these younger Midwestern leaders probably were closer to Earl Smith than to O'Neal.)

Though the Farm Bureau's emphasis on price policy as a means to promote the interests of farmers as producers was likely to lead to conflict with consumer groups and organizations,[6] Farm Bureau support (however equivocal) for greater freedom in international trade was in harmony with consumer interests. Even more closely in harmony with consumer interests was the Farm Bureau's support of antimonopoly measures. The Farm Bureau's traditional hostility to industrial monopolies was in abeyance during the early New Deal period, but when Thurman Arnold, as Assistant Attorney General in the Department of Justice, began to stress antitrust measures in 1938, he received some of his warmest support from the Farm Bureau. In explaining to O'Neal his philosophy on the antitrust laws, Arnold explicitly stated his intention of emphasizing the consumer interest, by which apparently he hoped to gain widespread support in the antitrust campaign.[7]

The drawing of definitive conclusions regarding the role of the A.F.B.F. in the making of national agricultural policy would require a study not only of the Farm Bureau and its relations to government, but also extensive research into the place and activities of

---

program, and against the Southern delegation, whose vote indicated a still solid attachment to that program. The motion read: "That Congress shall reserve the right to exercise this 'escape clause,' with respect to any agreement or provision thereof after such agreement becomes effective, by means of concurrent resolution by Congress."

[6] Illustrative of the frequent references by A.F.B.F. leaders to alleged "consumer dominance" of the Department of Agriculture is O'Neal's remark that the difficulty was "to get the consumer idea out of the heads of the Department." Telephone conversation between Congressman Cannon and O'Neal, May 21, 1941, A.F.B.F., O'Neal Papers (typescript).

[7] Arnold to O'Neal, August 26, 1940.

other farm organizations and other forces impinging on the policy-making process. Furthermore, the masterly skill of Franklin D. Roosevelt in using and balancing competing forces so as to keep the government more powerful than any of them[8] must be part of the perspective against which Farm Bureau influence is viewed. Nevertheless, even though it by no means offers a complete or final explanation, an intensive study of the Farm Bureau does throw considerable light on the processes by which national farm policy evolved in the period of the New Deal. During this critical period the A.F.B.F. was the most powerful of the national farm organizations.

By bridging over the historic sectional schism between Midwestern and Southern farmers, the A.F.B.F. made an important and perhaps even indispensable contribution to the New Deal for agriculture. It was only by establishing a high degree of unity within agriculture that sufficient strength could be maintained to enable agriculture to achieve compromises with other interest groups, such as labor and business, in the making of national economic policy.

A challenge to this interpretation of the Farm Bureau's role is found in the view that the Democratic Party itself, in the period from 1933 to 1940, was the chief agent through which sectional compromises were made and sectional unity achieved between the Midwestern and Southern farmers.

One cannot deny that the ultimate agencies through which compromises were achieved and policies made were political and governmental—the political parties, Congress, and the Administration. But an essential preliminary process of compromising and harmonizing the conflicts within agriculture was carried out during the early New Deal period chiefly through the A.F.B.F. under the leadership of Edward A. O'Neal. Further, the continual effort made by the Farm Bureau to obtain agreement among farmers was important in securing political support in Congress for policies sponsored by the Administration, and was important also in assuring the success of programs after legislative enactment.

To the question of whether the A.F.B.F. made the New Deal for agriculture or whether the New Deal for agriculture made the A.F.B.F., the answer is obviously that it was not as simple as all

[8] There is undoubtedly truth also in Burns's statement: "Indeed, Roosevelt to a surprising degree was captive to the political forces around him rather than their shaper." James MacGregor Burns, *Roosevelt, the Lion and the Fox* (London: Secker and Warburg, 1956), p. 403.

that. The Farm Bureau was one of several galaxies of forces. The weight of its influence was certainly great, and in its capacity as a cohesive agent the Farm Bureau gave significant aid to the Roosevelt administration during the early New Deal period. But when the A.F.B.F. showed signs of seeking to become the dominating force in agriculture,[9] the Department of Agriculture sought to restrain and balance its power. To Farm Bureau leaders it looked as if they were simply being denied the right of consultation on farm policy by the same Administration which had originally granted it.

If one thinks of history in terms of "an interplay between 'forces' and 'personalities,' "[10] the influence of Edward Asbury O'Neal was also significant. O'Neal's skill as a mediator was superbly used at an opportune time in history. Probably more than any other one person, he accomplished the healing of "that ancient breach"[11] between Midwestern and Southern farmers. The fact that the breach reopened later does not detract from his contribution to an epoch in history.

The Midwestern-Southern agrarian alliance which was cemented by the leadership of Ed O'Neal and Earl Smith was fostered by an overriding, impersonal force, the severest of economic depressions. As the depression lifted in some (but not all) areas of farming, unity showed signs of cracking. But the tradition of sectional compromise within the A.F.B.F. in itself formed a significant bridge between the sections. And the consciousness that farmers were declining in numbers and hence in potential influence relative to the rest of the American population might give the indispensable spur to cohesion, under new conditions and new leadership.

The men of O'Neal's stamp were considered agrarian liberals in the early New Deal period. The close informal alliance between them and the Department of Agriculture was a natural one in the phase when relief and recovery from depression were sought by the Roosevelt administration. Subsequently, as reform in agriculture assumed a larger place in New Deal thought, and as Henry A. Wallace and the Department of Agriculture moved to the left, O'Neal and his organization moved to the right. While (or perhaps even because) the A.F.B.F. continued to grow in membership and

---

[9] Rex Tugwell's plaint may be relevant here: "Our allies became more powerful than ourselves." Quoted in Arthur M. Schlesinger, Jr., *The Politics of Upheaval* (Boston: Houghton Mifflin Co., 1960), p. 391.

[10] Arnold J. Toynbee, "Seventeen 'Great Men'—or Great Forces," *New York Times Magazine,* November 8, 1959, p. 16.

[11] The term is Henry A. Wallace's, but not the final interpretation.

power, it was gradually being frozen out of the Department of Agriculture, and less apparently but more importantly out of the confidence of the President.

O'Neal himself was not an "organization man," not even a farm organization man, in any basic sense. He had a "cause," and that was American agriculture, to which even the Farm Bureau was subordinate. He was ruthless, but not unscrupulous, in pursuit of that cause.

Selected Bibliography 🌿 ‹‹‹‹

MANUSCRIPT COLLECTIONS

Alabama Farm Bureau files (Montgomery, Alabama). A few of these papers were used.

American Farm Bureau Federation files. These were located in the headquarters of the A.F.B.F. in Chicago. The most important ones used were the President O'Neal Papers. Some folders in this collection, which are not strictly the correspondence of President O'Neal but rather of his administration, are under such titles as "Midwest Conferences," or "regional files," or "research files." Also included in the A.F.B.F. records are the *Minutes of the Board of Directors*, the *Minutes of the Annual Meetings*, and the *Resolutions of the Annual Meetings*.

Babcock, Howard E. Papers, 1907-50. In Cornell University Library, Collection of Regional History and the University Archives.

Howard, James R. Papers. An unpublished manuscript of his memoirs and some other miscellaneous documents, such as a copy of *Equality for Agriculture*, were in the personal possession of Mr. Howard in Clemons, Iowa, when the author used them.

O'Neal, Edward A. Personal papers. A small collection of papers which were in O'Neal's possession in Florence, Alabama, when the author used them. These comprise some of his ancestral papers, and a few letters and documents which he particularly prized, such as several letters from Franklin D. Roosevelt.

U.S. Department of Agriculture papers. These are located in the National Archives, Washington, D.C. Especially useful were the Records of the Office of the Secretary of Agriculture, General Correspondence, 1933-40; and also the Agricultural Adjustment Administration Papers.

PERSONAL INTERVIEWS

Aaberg, Herman. May 17, 1949.
Appleby, Paul H. August 18, 1959.
Babcock, Howard E. March 21, 1949.
Howard, James R. June 22-23, 1949.
Kline, Allan B. January 18, May 2 and 17, 1949.
Ogg, W. R. April 12, 1949.

O'Neal, Edward A. May 23-24, 1949.
Randolph, Walter. May 26-27, 1949.
Shuman, Charles. July 25, 1949.
Smith, Earl C. July 18-19, 1949.
Tugwell, Rexford G. November 29, 1949.
Wallace, Henry A. August 27, 1959.
Wilson, M. L. August 18 and 29, 1959.

OTHER UNPUBLISHED SOURCES

Maddox, James G. "The Farm Security Administration." Unpublished
Ph.D. dissertation, Department of Economics, Harvard University,
1950.

NEWSPAPERS AND PERIODICALS

The Agricultural Situation. A publication of the U.S. Department of Agriculture.
American Agriculturist.
American Farm Bureau Federation Official News Letter. A weekly publication.
Bureau Farmer. A monthly publication of the A.F.B.F., which has been
succeeded by *The Nation's Agriculture.*
Cedar Rapids Gazette, May 10, 1935.
Cotton Trade Journal, January 27, 1945.
Illinois Agricultural Association Record. The official organ of the Illinois
Agricultural Association.
Michigan Farm News, February 4, 1933.
Montgomery Advertiser, September 9, 1937.
Prairie Farmer.
Producer's News (Plentywood, Montana), November 27, 1931.
Sioux City Journal, April 30, 1933.
United Farmer (New York Mills, Minnesota), October 6, 1930.
Wallace's Farmer.

PUBLIC DOCUMENTS

Farm Tenancy. Report of the President's Committee on Farm Tenancy,
February, 1937. Prepared under the auspices of the National Resources Committee. Washington: Government Printing Office, 1937.
U.S. Bureau of the Census. *Historical Statistics of the United States,
1789-1945.* Washington: Government Printing Office, 1949.
U.S. Congress, Joint Economic Committee. *Policy for Commercial Agriculture.* 85th Cong., 1st Sess., 1957.
U.S. *Congressional Record.*
U.S. Department of Agriculture, Office of the Secretary. Memorandum
No. 1368, November 24, 1954. This is the memorandum cutting the

198] *The Farm Bureau and the New Deal*

formal ties between employees of the U.S. Department of Agriculture and farm organizations.

U.S. House of Representatives, Committee on Appropriations. *Hearings on Agriculture Department Appropriation Bill for 1942. Part 2.* 77th Cong., 1st Sess., 1941.

U.S. House of Representatives, Committee on Appropriations. *Hearings on Agriculture Department Appropriation Bill for 1943. Part 2.* 77th Cong., 2d Sess., 1942.

U.S. House of Representatives, Committee on Appropriations. *Hearings on Agriculture Department Appropriation Bill for 1945.* 78th Cong., 2d Sess., 1944.

U.S. House of Representatives, Committee on Ways and Means. *Foreign Trade Policy.* Washington: Government Printing Office, 1958. A compendium of papers.

U.S. House of Representatives, Committee on Ways and Means. *Hearings on Extension of Reciprocal Trade Agreements Act. Part 2.* 76th Cong., 3d Sess., 1940.

U.S. Senate, Committee on the Judiciary. *Hearings on Lobby Investigation.* 71st Cong., 2d Sess., 1930.

BULLETINS

Bachman, Kenneth L., and Ronald W. Jones. *Size of Farms in the United States,* U.S. Department of Agriculture, Technical Bulletin No. 1011. Washington: Government Printing Office, July, 1950.

McElveen, Jackson V. *Family Farms in a Changing Economy,* U.S. Department of Agriculture, Agriculture Information Bulletin No. 171. Washington: Government Printing Office, March, 1957.

"The Role of the Land-Grant College in Governmental Agricultural Programs," *Iowa State College Bulletin,* Vol. XXXVIII (June 8, 1938).

U.S. Department of Agriculture. *Agricultural Adjustment Administration, 1937-38.* Washington: Government Printing Office, 1939.

U.S. Department of Agriculture. *Agricultural Adjustment Programs, 1933-41.* Washington: Government Printing Office, 1942.

U.S. Department of Agriculture. *Land Use Planning Under Way, July, 1940.* A booklet prepared by the Bureau of Agricultural Economics in co-operation with other agencies.

BOOKS

Baker, Gladys. *The County Agent.* Chicago: University of Chicago Press, 1939.

Benedict, Murray R. *Can We Solve the Farm Problem? An Analysis of Federal Aid to Agriculture.* New York: The Twentieth Century Fund, 1955.

———. *Farm Policies of the United States, 1790-1950: A Study of Their Origins and Development.* New York: The Twentieth Century Fund, 1953.

Black, John D. *Agricultural Reform in the United States.* New York: Mc-Graw-Hill Book Co., 1929.

————. *Parity, Parity, Parity.* Cambridge, Massachusetts: The Harvard Committee on Research in the Social Sciences, 1942.

Block, William J. *The Separation of the Farm Bureau and the Extension Service. Political Issue in a Federal System.* Illinois Studies in the Social Sciences, Vol. XLVII. Urbana: University of Illinois Press, 1960.

Burns, James MacGregor. *Roosevelt, the Lion and the Fox.* London: Secker and Warburg, 1956.

Capper, Arthur. *The Agricultural Bloc.* New York: Harcourt, Brace and Co., 1922.

Chambers, Clarke A. *California Farm Organizations.* Berkeley: University of California Press, 1952.

Christenson, Reo M. *The Brannan Plan: Farm Politics and Policy.* Ann Arbor: University of Michigan Press, 1959.

Davis, Joseph S. *On Agricultural Policy, 1926-1938.* Palo Alto, California: Stanford University Food Research Institute, 1939.

Davis, P. O. *One Man: Edward Asbury O'Neal III of Alabama.* Auburn: Alabama Polytechnic Institute, 1945.

The Federalist. Modern Library Edition. New York: Random House, 1937.

Fite, Gilbert C. *George N. Peek and the Fight for Farm Parity.* Norman: University of Oklahoma Press, 1954.

Galbraith, J. K. *American Capitalism: The Concept of Countervailing Power.* Boston: Houghton Mifflin Co., 1952.

Gaus, John M., and Leon D. Wolcott. *Public Administration and the United States Department of Agriculture.* Chicago: Public Administration Service, 1940.

Halcrow, Harold G. *Agricultural Policy of the United States.* New York: Prentice-Hall, 1953.

Hardin, Charles M. *Freedom in Agricultural Education.* Chicago: University of Chicago Press, 1955.

————. *The Politics of Agriculture.* Glencoe, Illinois: The Free Press, 1952.

Hicks, John D. *The Populist Revolt.* Minneapolis: University of Minnesota Press, 1931.

Hutchinson, William T. *Lowden of Illinois.* 2 vols. Chicago: University of Chicago Press, 1957.

Kile, Orville M. *The Farm Bureau Movement.* New York: Macmillan Co., 1921.

————. *The Farm Bureau Through Three Decades.* Baltimore: The Waverley Press, 1948.

Kramer, Dale. *The Truth About the Farm Bureau.* Falls Church, Virginia: National Affairs Press, 1950.

Lord, Russell. *The Agrarian Revival: A Study of Agricultural Extension.* New York: American Association for Adult Education, 1939.

————. *The Wallaces of Iowa.* Boston: Houghton Mifflin Co., 1947.

McConnell, Grant. *The Decline of Agrarian Democracy.* Berkeley: University of California Press, 1953.

McCune, Wesley. *The Farm Bloc.* Garden City, New York: Doubleday, Doran and Co., 1943.

————. *Who's Behind Our Farm Policy?* New York: Frederick A. Praeger, 1956.

Mighell, Ronald L. *American Agriculture: Its Structure and Place in the Economy.* New York: John Wiley and Sons, 1955.

[Peek, George N., and Hugh S. Johnson.] *Equality for Agriculture.* H. W. Harrington, 1922.

Pritchett, C. Herman. *The Tennessee Valley Authority: A Study in Public Administration.* Chapel Hill: University of North Carolina Press, 1943.

Saloutos, Theodore. *Farmer Movements in the South, 1865-1933.* Berkeley: University of California Press, 1960.

————, and John D. Hicks. *Agricultural Discontent in the Middle West, 1900-1939.* Madison: University of Wisconsin Press, 1951.

Schlesinger, Arthur M., Jr. *The Coming of the New Deal.* Boston: Houghton Mifflin Co., 1959.

————. *The Politics of Upheaval.* Boston: Houghton Mifflin Co., 1960.

Selznick, Philip. *T.V.A. and the Grass Roots: A Study in the Sociology of Formal Organization.* University of California Publications in Culture and Society, Vol. III. Berkeley: University of California Press, 1949.

Shideler, James H. *Farm Crisis, 1919-1923.* Berkeley: University of California Press, 1957.

Spillman, W. J. *Balancing the Farm Output.* New York: Orange Judd Publishing Co., 1927.

Taylor, Carl C. *The Farmers' Movement, 1620-1920.* New York: American Book Co., 1953.

Turner, Frederick Jackson. *The Significance of Sections in American History.* Gloucester, Mass.: Peter Smith, 1950.

Wallace, Henry A. *New Frontiers.* New York: Reynal and Hitchcock, 1934.

ARTICLES

Albjerg, Victor L. "Allan Blair Kline: The Farm Bureau, 1955," *Current History,* XXVIII (June, 1955), 362-68.

Allin, Bushrod W. "County Planning Project—a Co-operative Approach to Agricultural Planning," *Journal of Farm Economics,* XXII (February, 1940), 292-301.

Carleton, William G. "Gray Silver and the Rise of the Farm Bureau," *Current History,* XXVIII (June, 1955), 343-50.

Crawford, J. G., and Gunnar Lange. "County Planning for Land-Use Adjustment," *Journal of Farm Economics,* XXII (May, 1940), 473-92.

Davis, Chester C. "The Development of Agricultural Policy Since the End of the World War," in *Farmers in a Changing World,* Yearbook of the U.S. Department of Agriculture for 1940 (Washington: Government Printing Office, 1940), pp. 297-326.

Edwards, Everett E. "American Agriculture—the First 300 Years," in *Farmers in a Changing World,* Yearbook of the U.S. Department of Agriculture for 1940 (Washington: Government Printing Office, 1940), pp. 171-276.

"The Farm Bureau," *Fortune,* June, 1944, pp. 156 ff.

"The Fortune Survey: Farmers II," *Fortune,* April, 1943, pp. 8 ff.

Gregory, Clifford V. "The American Farm Bureau Federation and the A.A.A.," in Childs, Harwood L. (ed.), *Pressure Groups and Propaganda* (Annals of the American Academy of Political and Social Science, Vol. CLXXIX [May, 1935]).

Gross, Neal C. "A Post-Mortem on County Planning," *Journal of Farm Economics,* XXV (August, 1943), 644-61.

Hardin, Charles M. "The Bureau of Agricultural Economics Under Fire: A Study in Valuation Conflicts," *Journal of Farm Economics,* XXVIII (August, 1946), 635-68.

Kirkendall, Richard S. "Four Economists in the Political Process," *Journal of Farm Economics,* XLI (May, 1959), 194-210.

Saloutos, Theodore. "The American Farm Bureau Federation and Farm Policy: 1933-1945," *The Southwestern Social Science Quarterly,* XXVIII (March, 1947), No. 4, 314-33.

————. "Edward A. O'Neal: The Farm Bureau and the New Deal," *Current History,* XXVIII (June, 1955), 356-61.

Tolley, H. R. "The Conservation Program and the Extension Service," *Proceedings of the Association of Land-Grant Colleges and Universities,* 1936, pp. 190-91.

————. "The Farmer, the College, the Department of Agriculture— Their Changing Relationships," *Proceedings of the Association of Land-Grant Colleges and Universities,* 1936, pp. 70-76.

Toynbee, Arnold J. "Seventeen 'Great Men'—or Great Forces," *New York Times Magazine,* November 8, 1959, pp. 16 ff.

Tugwell, Rexford G. "The Resettlement Idea," *Agricultural History,* XXXIII (October, 1959), 159-64.

Wilson, M. L. "Facets of County Planning: On Using Democracy," *Land Policy Review,* II (January-February, 1939), 1-4.